P9-CNI-529

The Fishers of Men

The Fishers of Men

By Michele Saponaro

Translated from the Italian

Hawthorn Books, Inc.

Publishers   *New York City*

FIRST EDITION, *October, 1962*

H—3166

Contents

6

The Fishers of Men

1

Jesus Reappears

Only the young redeemed sinner Mary Magdalen had seen Him and heard His voice.

She did not see His face but only a shadow falling across her shoulder. It was the shadow of a tall man, and the rising sun stretched it out over the length of the field. At first she thought it was a farmer; then she recognized the gentle Master from His voice as He called her name softly: "Mary—." Lifting her tearful face from her palms she turned to look at Him, but there was no one there. The Master had disappeared. She may have seen the white form melting away, dissolved by the morning light as mist is dispersed by the sun.

No other woman had seen Him. None of the disciples. Probably not even the Mother.

Mary told the others that Jesus was not dead: He still lived; He had appeared to her and had spoken to her. She found them all together in her house at Bethany: they were worn out by sorrow and by the hopeless anguish of the long night. There were also the Mother, her cousin Mary of Cleophas, and Sa-

9

lome, mother of James and John. Martha, Mary's sister, was baking bread. When Lazarus, the young man of the last miracle, heard her story, he went outside and looked all around the house, even jumping up onto the rocks to peer, with hands shading his eyes, to the farthest horizons beyond the city, now rising in a nimbus of gold. He, too, was looking for the white shade of the Master which had appeared to his sister and then dissolved.

The eleven were either sitting by the table or in the courtyard in the early morning sun, waiting for they knew not what, between disbelief and hope, the way the relatives and friends of a dear departed one always wait. But fatigue, sleeplessness, and fasting extinguish all hope, changing it into a bleak resignation, turning disbelief into an apprehensive fear.

After all, the feeling of guilt depresses and humiliates more than any other anxiety: and all eleven felt they were guilty of allowing the Master to be killed, of actually killing Him with their own hands since they had been unable to defend Him with their own hands. By fleeing they had made themselves accomplices of the traitor. A few days before, when the Master had been called to the deathbed of Lazarus and had left tranquil Perea to return to the lion's den, Jerusalem, Thomas had said: "Let's die with Him!" But, when the hour came, no one had known how to die for Him.

Now they sat, looking at their knees, and no one spoke. They did not even dare to raise their heads to look at one another, because each one feared to read his own self-reproach in the eyes of another.

Like Mary, Peter and John had also seen the tomb uncovered, but they understood nothing of the great mystery which had taken place on Easter night in the secret of that tomb. They still trembled at its strangeness with fear and wonder.

Thomas, the ardent skeptic who had wanted to die with

Him, must have been thinking of a way to follow Him, to join Him in death: he saw no other way of finding his gentle Master again.

They awakened at Mary's announcement. Quickly they crowded around her as the young woman's joyous cry rang through the rugged mountain clefts: "I saw the Master! I saw the Master!" The east wind carried the cry to the city newly roused from the torpor that had followed the debauch. The eleven heard her, and so did the pious women, the shepherds, the wayfarers, the merchants, and the pilgrims who, in procession, were leaving the Holy City to return to their villages. But no one knew that Mary Magdalen's cry was renewing the atmosphere of the earth and filling it with a new sense of life. No one knew that her cry would remain eternally suspended in the air of the world—a spiritual dust.

All the day before and all that long night, Peter's sobs had murmured quietly throughout Jerusalem—the sobs of his broken and disconsolate weeping after the cockcrow—the sounds of that weeping would also assist Magdalen's happy cry in the renewal of the world.

They decided to return to the city: not only the eleven, for now the other disciples came out of hiding, where they had fled from the synod's anger and the spectacle of the three crosses over Calvary. Remorsefully, they thought of sacrifice as an act of expiation, and now the marvel of the new announcement gave them heart. Curiosity also made them heedless of danger. They were ready to defy priests and Pharisees, but they met none, and those who yesterday were armed with hatred now let them pass indifferently. There was no longer any reason for the synod to fear that handful of frightened youths, inoffensive and leaderless.

Each one took his own path into the city, for they were

curious to gather news and gossip from all the scattered huts. But they found little because the city was resting in the satiety and numbness that always follows a holiday.

What had happened the day before was not even remembered by those who had been present, except perhaps as an evening at the theatre is vaguely remembered the following day. The greater part of the enormous crowd which had gathered from near and far were unaware of the spectacle that had occurred. For them, an ordinary administrative act had taken place, a trial and a torture, nothing else. So many had occurred before this, and a tomb always buried everything.

The synod had every reason to minimize the execution of Jesus, lest a malefactor become a hero, an outlaw a martyr. Therefore, they did not persecute the disciples, or even try to harm them. Even if they saw them return to the city, or heard about it, still they let them alone. They could not permit themselves to be afraid of them: they had to appear unafraid in order to prove the condemnation an act of justice, not one of rancor or revenge. After all, the disciples had only listened; it was Jesus who had spoken and acted. Ignorant, deluded, bewitched—Jesus had said He was a miracleworker. And once the dangerous one had been eliminated, it seemed a good policy to be indulgent with His artless and inactive confederates.

After their return to the city, the disciples reunited in the friendly house where they had been welcomed with the Master for the Last Supper. Owned by a woman who was also named Mary, it was situated quite far from the Temple and from Calvary at the opposite end of the city, but its very distance made it a safer refuge. News was provided from the nearby palace of the High Priest, which bustled at every hour of the day with a convention of men, business, and monkey business.

The disciples did not know how to proceed or what they should do next. For three years they had lived an unbelievable life, uprooted from the earth, suspended in a world of faith and trust, following a guide who promised to lead them to an arcane kingdom of power and felicity, which signified freedom from the thralldom of the Roman Empire: but it signified something more too.

They had been taken away from earth and raised toward heaven; now reality had suddenly thrust them back to the ground. They were like orphans abandoned by a father. What to do? Where to go? The column of light that had guided them from Galilee to Jerusalem had now gone out, and they no longer had eyes to see the future.

"The light is come into the world," John would say one day, but now there was only darkness before their eyes. More than anything else, they felt disoriented, not hearing His words, not seeing them transposed into action. There was nothing for them to do but to return to Galilee to their mothers and other relatives, to their wives if they were married, to their boats and nets, to the lathe and the loom. The publican would return to his ledger and his taxes. In any event, they had to resume their old lives of slavery, because the liberation had been only a dream.

The disciples sat down to the table that evening in the house where they had eaten the Last Supper, but they were not all present. Thomas was missing.

Two young men knocked at the door, and they had a wondrous tale to tell. They were two of that hundred or so anonymous disciples who had followed Jesus without being received into the family of the apostles: Jesus had sent them also, on occasion, to preach the Good News. Now these two youths spoke of meeting Jesus the day before in the villages of Emmaus, several miles from Jerusalem. They had been walking briskly along, as if to escape from the incubus which weighed on them in the city, mournfully reviewing the sad event which had bloodied the sacred Paschal feast with innocent blood. For them, nothing so terrible and awesome had happened in many years: even though the synod tried to reduce it to an act within the confines of normal judicial process, an uneasy terror was rising among the people.

A man who walked down the same road, almost following them as if to eavesdrop on their conversation, approached them and asked what they were discussing. Was he a foreigner? And even if he was, how did it happen that he did not know that a trial and a torture had occurred these past days; that Annas, Caiaphas, and Pilate had put the great prophet Jesus of Nazareth to the cross for proclaiming Israel's liberation from the power of Rome. Everybody knew this; though few knew what had happened afterward. The next day, at sunrise, women and some disciples had gone to the Master's sepulcher to pray and weep, and they had found it uncovered and empty. The Master's body was no longer there; there were angels, apparitions. . . .

The unknown wayfarer walked quietly along with them; he only said that there was nothing new or extraordinary in what they said, because it all had been predicted long before by the prophets. When they reached the village they stopped, and he said goodbye, planning to continue his journey. But, since it was already evening, they suggested he rest too, and they invited him to share their supper.

They sat together at the table. Then their eyes were opened. How was it that they had not recognized His face before, or had they been unable to see Him? Now, as He sat between them, they recognized the way His hands broke the bread and divided it: just as He had done on the woeful evening of the Last Supper, as He had done at joyous repasts in the meadows, between the telling of a parable and an admonish-

14

ment. They recognized Jesus: it was Jesus. And He was alive.

While the two youths told of the marvelous encounter, Mary, the mistress of the house, had closed the door against the indiscreet and the evil-minded. "Be wary as the serpents," the Master had said, "Guard yourselves from the men who do not love you!," and now more than ever it was necessary to heed His prudent counsel. Then, they too, would be gentle as doves.

Suddenly, lo and behold, Jesus was sitting with them here too. Were their eyes clouded by lack of sleep? No, it was truly He. He had come in without anyone opening the door for Him. They heard His loved voice repeating His usual greeting, "Peace be with you!" They saw His hands break the bread, bless it, and distribute it. The unforgettable gesture of His hands! He asked for something to eat, and they offered Him what they had—fish roasted over the coals and a comb of honey. Then He spoke, gazing in turn into each man's eyes: "Why are you troubled? Of what are you afraid? Do you doubt that it is I?"

It was not easy for them to keep their senses in the face of such unbelievable and extraordinary happenings. They remained quiet because they could find no words in the tongue of man to answer Him.

"It is truly I. Look at My wounds. Touch My flesh and bones."

Then, suddenly as He had come, He disappeared, leaving the disciples stunned and speechless. Only Thomas had not been present at His appearance, and when they told him about it he would not believe it. He could not: men who believe without having seen are no longer men, they are saints.

Thomas' incredulity was not due to a lack of affection. Doubt arises from fear, and fear is the child of love—of great love and sorrow. The more one loves the more one fears, and

Thomas certainly loved his Master the way one loves a father: with the tenderness, the trepidation, and the anxiety of a child. Thomas was not the skeptical and suspicious disciple of later fame; on the contrary, he worshipped and adored Jesus. But he did not dare to believe; he tried to avoid the danger, the temptation, because he felt his soul falter at the thought of withstanding a still greater disappointment. If Jesus appeared to him only to abandon him all over again, what would become of a poor lost child such as he?

And Jesus did appear again, after eight days. He chose Thomas from among the disciples seated at home, and took his hands and held them to His forehead and breast so that the doubter could feel the forehead wounded by the thorns of the mock crown, and the breast torn by the centurion's lance. The blood had coagulated on these wounds: Thomas believed. He realized that the Master was not a mere mortal like himself, or like Peter, John, James, or the others, because though His body was like the body of Peter and John and James, His Spirit was divine, It was God.

After these appearances, Jesus again disappeared, and the disciples went to Galilee, hoping to find Him again among those pleasant hills, as He had once predicted to them. It was not a happy return for those who had left Galilee to conquer a kingdom: it was more like a retreat, a rout. But, it was necessary to earn their daily bread.

They tried to rearrange their domestic affairs, unsettled by the beautiful adventure which had ended so sorrowfully, to reconcile themselves to the old houses they had deserted, to reaccustom themselves to the habits of family needs and affections.

In their memories they would retrace the days spent under the Master's guidance, days so brief, but filled with marvels.

They repeated the great words of love they had heard from His lips, words which filled their minds and hearts like a quivering song, a will to great works; and they were made stronger and better by those memories, quickened by a new life.

In their silences, they heard again that divine voice which had once held them spellbound, and had terrified them too, on occasion. Around the lake of Genezaret and among the pleasant hills of Nazareth and Cana, the air bloomed with that voice as the meadows of springtime once again bloomed with buttercups and poppies.

The resurrected Master had disappeared once again; perhaps they would never again see Him, but His presence was renewed at every step of their toilsome lives, and His luminous eyes looked out at them from every familiar face, watching their every action like a guide—a warning, a spur. A new spirit had entered into the bodies of those fishermen, artisans, and peasants, and they felt that this new spirit gave their actions a meaning and a scope.

Then Jesus appeared once more to them; once again before they were to see Him finally withdraw from the ways of the earth, wafting away among the stars and clouds of Heaven. He sat among them in the place of their first meetings for the Master wanted to part from His disciples in that spot where He had first gathered them together one by one. They had gone back to fishing, so He waited for them at the lake shore. He filled their nets with fish, as He had done one earlier day in Peter's boat. He roasted the carp over the coals with His own hands, and ate it with them. Then he gave to Peter His last will and testament, imparting to him, and to the others, advice and orders on how they were to carry the Good News into the world.

Peter was the oldest disciple, and the spiritual eldest son. He was not the most educated, but he had the most ardent heart. He had denied the Master in the hour of supreme peril, but was that not confusion imposed on him by God to make him the most faithful of the disciples, ready for the supreme sacrifice? To Simon Peter, Jesus entrusted the task of heading the work He had begun, that of leading mankind toward freedom.

Then Simon Peter reached his old boat again, and put down his nets, never again to take them up. His brother Andrew did the same, as did Zebedee's sons. Philip and Thomas left the tools of their trade to their relatives; Nathanael and Matthew collected their savings. The relatives of Jesus too, James, Judah, and Simon, who had not been the most active or the most believing of the disciples who had made the group of twelve by joining it in the last year, now closed their workshop, sold their fields, and followed Peter.

The little congregation which until yesterday had been united solely by the Master's authority was now cemented by solidarity and faith. From the synagogue at Capharnaum, where they had gathered together for a last prayer, they set off on the road to Jerusalem.

They realized their destiny. They must leave this tranquil land for the city of struggle and danger. These poor folk had a precious treasure, a wealth which they were to spread throughout the world. Farewell to Galilee, land of golden skies and vine-laden valleys, where for the first time the hymn of the holy revolution was heard: "Have you heard what was told by the ancients? But I tell you. . . ."

No one knew that the echo of those words, borne by the winds to the four horizons, was to change the face of the earth inhabited by men.

The eleven reached Jerusalem after the Feast of Tabernacles, and they took up residence in the great house of the Last Supper. The season of the year, still chilly, encouraged secret reunions and the formation of a plan of action. As a first act of obedience to the Master, the company decided to reconstitute itself and elect a twelfth brother to replace the betrayor. They chose two; Joseph Barsabas, called the Just, and Matthias. They let Jesus decide between the two by casting lots, and the lot fell on Matthias.

Disciples came from all over to follow the supporters of Jesus, and though they had been only a hundred and twenty at the Master's death, in a few months, they had already risen to five hundred. They called themselves brethren. Other people called them Nazarenes.

2

The First Christian Community

They were already changed men. They were unaware of the new spirit which breathed in the world, because it had worked an equal change in them, and in their concept of virtue and the other laws of life. A burning spirit, like a sudden great flame, had been lit in them and they were transported into the supernatural.

No longer did they consider themselves fishermen and workmen, slaves of their daily labor and their mediocre needs, destined to exhaust themselves in that labor and in those needs. They were called to a mission, uprooted from daily routine. Their sentiments were still confused, not so much as a conscious state but as a permeation of exaltation which kept them in a state of rapture: they could not yet have the conviction of principle.

The nearly three years of training they had at the elevated school of Jesus had refined and enlightened them. Day by day, without realizing it, they had been filled with advice and ideas which they began to define and evaluate only now. Their memories were granaries in which they had placed all the wheat reaped in the steps of the Great Sower. They had only to reach into that granary, and they found enough to assuage the hunger of masses of starvelings, let alone the five thousand in the hills of Bethsaida.

O Divine Words heard on the Mount in that May night flowering with stars! Marvels of advice and encouragement, of invocation and prohibition which will come to be called the Beatitudes! They separated the chaff from the wheat in their nascent thoughts. The unforeseen and profound replies to their questions, to the curiosity of passersby and beggars, the serene and sovereign ways of convincing doubters and dominating opponents, the acts of severity or indulgence that were always just: how many they were!

And the parables told with an allusive and secret language, like that of conspirators, so that only they could understand: "Let him who has ears to hear, listen. . . ." They surprised one another by repeating those words, attempting those gestures. They repeated them to the curious around them, as if of their own volition, perhaps without realizing that Jesus spoke through their voices, and the astonished listeners admired the wisdom of those Galilean fishermen and workmen. Peter, most of all, spoke freely, ardently, and courageously, assuming the leadership which had been entrusted to him. The others recognized him as their leader without envy.

The rebirth which had taken place in them had originated in their hearts; now it extended to their mental faculties. It made them superior beings. They were certain that the Divine Spirit of the Master spoke and operated through them when one day they were invaded by the sacred fire of the Oracle and of martyrdom.

The Feast of Pentecost was being celebrated at Jerusalem and, as usual, the twelve had gathered at the house of Mary.

A sudden storm seemed to be unleashed, one of those turbulent May storms that often swell up in Palestine at mid-day: the air becomes heavy with darkness, thunder and lightning, but no rain comes to give freshness and relief. The house was enveloped by strong winds and lightning flashes and the disciples saw tongues of flame: from the ceiling the flames sank down over their heads and remained there—the baptism by fire predicted by the Master, the descent of the Holy Spirit into their mortal souls. Infused with that fire they spoke to the crowd which had taken shelter in the house and courtyard. They raised their voices in tongues they did not know; which they had never before spoken. There were pilgrims who had come from every land in Asia and Greece, and each was able to listen in his own tongue. Peter made a long and eloquent speech, evoking anew the earthly life of Jesus, explaining to the audience that He was the Messiah sent by God to liberate Israel. The crowd thought them astrologers, or drunk with wine.

Mary's house now became the nest of conspiracy and the altar of prayer. This Mary may have been a relative of John and James, sons of Zebedee, or a family friend. She had a youthful son, named Mark, who was especially attached to Simon Peter, the recognized leader. Everyone slept where he could, but they all met around the same table at suppertime. And now there was no lack of huts and houses in which to find a resting place.

Those of the disciples who had some property to sell and who had sold it and those who had some savings which they had collected brought the money and it was placed in a common fund. It was the way of life initiated by Jesus: they felt it must be continued. They had all they needed, and the money was distributed by the leaders to each according to his need. It was the little money which made up the wages of a good soldier. Now they no longer bothered to remain hidden and to dissimulate for there was no longer fear or doubt in their hearts. Pentecost had inspired those unarmed men with a superhuman courage.

This simple unworried poverty brought them serene joy. Able to enjoy the beauties of nature undisturbed, unweighed by the existence of grave needs, these unlettered men had realized the Utopia of a religious communism long before man invented the theory at the same time he invented the machine. Because they no longer had families of their own, or did not find this enough, they created a larger family of brothers and sisters outside the flesh—the religious community.

After a year or two the five hundred had become three thousand, and in that time the land of Israel was really the abode of earthly paradise. "The multitude of believers were of one heart and soul," the historian of the apostles was to write later, "and not one of them said anything of his possessions was his alone, but they had all things in common." Nicodemus, the man of riches without end, certainly underwrote a great part of the many needs of that first community. Cluza's wife, Joanna, who had helped the Master so much by selling her jewels, continued to assist the disciples.

The twelve remained in Mary's house, while the others found shelter with other kindly and prosperous housewives. The dinner hour was the happiest time of day. It was also the hour of prayers and reminiscences. The modest meal began with a prayer and reminiscenses followed it. Mingled with the recollections of times past were the accounts of things seen and accomplished during the present day. They had gone with the sun from house to house, from tent to tent, pilgrims of a new world. In the evening each one reported on his day's work and asked instructions for the next day. The first efforts brought the apostles masses of neophytes, and no day was complete that did not end with a new baptism and a new conversion.

Little by little, the supper became a rite, and the agape, divesting itself of its bodily associations, was elevated to a sacred symbol. The essentials of the table were furnished by the community: everyone who was able brought something to share with his neighbors. The memory of the piece of bread, of Jesus' hands breaking the loaf to distribute it to His children, that gesture which was their most vivid image of the Master, along with the arcane words which had accompanied that gesture, made them decide to give the supper a deep religious sense of communion with Jesus, with God, and thus was born the practice of the Eucharist. Every day it followed the fraternal meal; later it would be reserved to one day only, that which followed the Hebrew Sabbath and became the Lord's day, the Holy Day of the new religion.

Thus life was still idyllic in Jerusalem, and the authorities of the synod and of Rome did not interfere. Harmony and joy flourished in that land irrigated by love, and they were the most persuasive arguments for the new religion's doctrines. Women were especially helpful to these poor preachers, just as they had been to Jesus.

The women of the near Orient age early. They lose the freshness of youth quickly: by twenty-five they are already careworn. Now, in the words of the Good News, they found a different youth consisting of serene good works and joyous hope. The widows, who under the law of old had been almost rejected, now felt themselves venerated with the Mother, as if sanctified. The women experienced a singular attraction of sense and spirit combined for those strong young men who lived a life of chastity and rigor.

Shy ways, modest thoughts, and words clear as the eye of the speaker, are considerably more persuasive to budding womanhood than are flowery speeches. There also was the attraction of the other women who had known Jesus—Mary, Martha,

Salome, and Joanna. They had followed Him and served Him; they were pardoned and defended by Him; they anointed His weary feet and His burning forehead with soothing ointment; they wept and rejoiced for Him; they saw His death and His resurrection. O gentle reverie, to listen to that glorious story recounted by their melodious voices!

If the preaching of Peter, John, James and the other active and eloquent disciples was efficacious in gathering and instructing new members, the presence of these pious women who guarded the divine gift of grace in their hearts, almost perpetuating the presence of Jesus in Jerusalem, was certainly not less so. They had heard words and received confidences from the Master which the men did not even know had been uttered. Jesus, rising from the tomb, had said His first word to one of these women—her name—"Mary . . ." and no other words had been needed.

That woman who had lived in sin, the venal prey of filthy appetites, had been purified at the feet of Jesus as if in a flame of sanctity. Other sinners had been cleansed of every strain, as the laundress cleans the criminal's bloody clothes in the waters of a mountain spring. An adulteress had been saved from stoning. A woman of Samaria had left her five husbands. Now maidens, wives, and widows sought out these privileged women to hear them tell in their own words the miraculous works wrought by the Master, and each one seemed to see the Master's reflection in their eyes. They found happiness in being with these women, even if it was only for a little while. They envied them, but tenderly asked to serve them. And it was certainly they who nourished the undying taper with their devotion. They also sought out the Mother and served Her.

Jerusalem was a vast melting pot of Jews from every land, native-born and alien, all or part Jewish. The central nucleus was formed by the townspeople themselves, strict Pharisees rooted in the law which was their moral force, and profiteering and unbelieving Sadducees, clinging to the morality of privilege and taxation. Around this nucleus, which was destined to shrink constantly as it became more rigid, Roman expansion and the currents of commerce brought in a perpetual intrusive immigration of various peoples. There were pagans converted to the Jewish monotheism and there were Jews dispersed by the periodic persecutions, who for reasons of faith or business returned from every part of the Diaspora, bringing with them their mixed families.

The desire for the motherland was always strong among the Jews, a mournful nostalgia for the Holy City, for the temple where they felt closer to their God. Now these Hellenized Jews, from Syria, Cyrenaica, Egypt, and the Asian provinces, brought western ideas to Jerusalem along with the Greek language. They had formed communities apart from the local community; they lived in separate neighborhoods, constructing their own synagogues in what seemed a large number in this dawning era of Christianity.

These people, more than the others, took an interest in the new discussions. With unsuspicious curiosity, they observed the twelve young missionaries who called themselves the apostles, and their following of some thousands of other persons known as Nazarenes. Since they were not motivated by the jealousy produced by daily attrition, they were able to enter into their conversations and to become intimately acquainted with the clear simplicity of feeling of that brethren. They were better able to understand them too, because their ideas had been broadened by their travels and their relationships with various races and beliefs.

In a truly singular century of the history of civilization, when the world was filled with the strangest words—confused survivals of a philosophy long still because it had said all that it had to say—the dispersed Jews were accustomed to the most bizarre ideas. But the arcane events which the new believers recounted with a gentle conviction were such that they impressed these people profoundly. The disciples seemed to walk with their heads in the clouds when they voiced those inspired words, as if they obeyed celestial visions and instructions, but in their actions their feet were planted firmly on the ground. One had no choice but to love these Nazarenes who preached love and sang praises of poverty. Even as the Nazarenes grew trustingly near the Hellenists, they sought among them both support and a field for action.

In fact, the first conversions came from the Jews of the Diaspora; it was this which helped to distract the attention of the synod. For a year or two, the pioneers thus were able to work in the shadows, without giving umbrage to the resentful priests. The priests were almost unaware of the spread of the new religion; it had not yet encroached on their interests, their prerogatives, or their pride. It was as a small stream bubbling in a narrow bed, and it did not yet threaten to overflow. The new believers assembled in the temple too, but they spoke about charity and also inspired this charity in those who listened to them.

Without going beyond its banks, this stream irrigated the field. There occurred in the human field of Palestine what takes place in every earthly field which is watered by a stream: the moisture from its shores spread from sod to sod throughout the entire field. Those neophytes now drank in the words of the first disciples as the first disciples had absorbed them from the Master. The Sermon on the Mount penetrated and was propagated, resounding from the synagogues and marketplaces. The very mysterious parables reflowered and were multiplied at every meeting. They were repeated from memory; those who were present told them to those who had been absent, varying the themes with their own imagination, and thus were shaped the first stones of the necklace of legends which the old were to conserve and the young to disseminate.

Day by day Matthew rearranged the notes he had taken. Mark, the youth who may have glimpsed Christ only once—on the night of Gethsemane—asked Peter to tell him more of all the miracles which the Master had wrought, and he listened to this man whom the Master had placed in charge of the community as one listens to a father.

There were no wealthy men in this first community; they lived in absolute poverty, limiting their needs and asking charity of those who were able to give it. These disciples who had heard the sermon of the lilies of the field and the birds of the air perfected the Essene hermits' way of life, which was the most rigid application of the Mosaic Law. And if the Son of Man had not always had a roof to shelter Him and a stone on which to rest His head, how could they envy the comforts and pleasures of the rich? Among them there were men of much intellect, much education, and of active will. Of these Stephen and Barnabas immediately shone forth.

Joseph the Levite, a native of Cyprus, was surnamed Barnabas, which means the son of consolation or the son of exhortation. A Hellenite Jew, he may have been studying in Jerusalem at the time of the teaching of Jesus and of the trial, but he emerged only now from obscurity as he came to the apostles and offered them his faith, his work, and his material wealth. He sold a farm he owned on Cyprus and turned the money over to the common fund. He was distinguished by his cultivated intellect, his open and incisive spirit, the fairness of his judgment, and the courtesy of his ways and words. He brought a plentitude of liberal ideas into the new church, which was still bound tightly to the temple, and the more advanced young people grouped themselves around him. He appears at once as the most enlightened among the new men.

Stephen was a young man of the same sort, but of a more ardent and aggressive disposition. He also came from a family of dispersed Jews, and he had undergone a thorough education at the school of Jerusalem. But, as it always happens in a time of action, it was his eloquence more than his learning that brought him to the front rank. He had the gift of language that draws and exalts; therefore, they elected him to the college of the seven deacons, the preachers and healers.

He preached in the synagogues of the Hellenite Jews and of the proselytes, the latter being pagans recently converted to Judaism. He preached particularly in a synagogue called the Synagogue of the Freedmen, where there were people from Cyrene, Alexandria, Ephesus, and Cilicia. He had a talent for debate and sought for adversaries to confound. He argued fiercely with another young man, his equal in age, culture, and polemic ardor, who also came from the Hellenist tradition, but who was a most rigid and zealous upholder of the Law, one Saul.

For Stephen, the Law was a chain that must be broken. He preached in the synagogues and in the temple because he needed a meeting place and the habits of the people were such that they congregated there, but he would have liked to tear down every wall so that his voice could spread out into the open air. He had adopted for himself one of the sayings of Jesus which had been told to him by the disciples, and he cried to all the winds: "God does not dwell in houses built by the hands of men."

3

The Wheat Spreads

The idyll could not long endure, especially when threatened by poverty and the ills it brings, suspiciousness and the little slynesses to which people resort for their own protection. Perhaps there was danger in their success which far outreached the hopes and ambitions of the founders.

There were few who owned property and sold it to bring money to the joint fund, and there were many for whom there was no provision, who needed everything. Nor were those who joined the group for aid alone scarce, and it was necessary to accept them also because out of the harvest of mercy the bold are often born.

But rivalry, jealousy, and discontent lurk where no one has power to multiply the loaves and the fishes. In the distribution of goods it happened that the native-born Jews received the larger share, or so it seemed to those who came from other lands. A group of widows of converted Greeks complained especially that they were neglected.

The twelve, too busy with the care of souls to pay close attention to the care of bodies, could not be aware of the little injustices which occurred on the outskirts of the community. They listened to the complaints of the widows, promised justice, and decided to institute a college of judges to oversee the administration of the community. There were seven, and they were called deacons: Stephen, Phillip, Prochorus, Nicanor, Timon, Parmenas, and Nicholas. All seven were Grecians recently converted to the new faith. The Palestinean Nazarenes, with a shrewd and cautious diplomacy, had excluded themselves from this college of deacons since the leaders, the twelve, were all Palestinians, and such a practice seemed fair. In this way was born the first ecclesiastical function and the first such institution. Thus the new community became centralized, facilitating its activity by the distribution of labor. The germ of wheat was sprouting.

Sharply divided from the evangelizers, these administrators and economists were called upon to solve every practical question arising from the diffusion of ideas. The aspirations of the spirit must not suffer the delays of the necessities of daily life. In this way, the care and teaching of the poor was elevated to the level of religious office. When new communities were founded in other places, every one of them was to have its college of deacons. It was the first level of a hierarchical construction whose future heights could not yet be known or foreseen. They would be achieved by time, one after another, as the spiritual interests, the practical necessities, the multiplication of churches and the need to defend them from outside threats and discipline them from within, fashioned the great structure. Meanwhile, relieved of the weight of these daily problems, the twelve could dedicate themselves wholly to preaching and sowing the good seed outside the little field of Jerusalem.

The lands populated by Jews were much larger than that little field; in fact, they could be said to reach the limits of the known world, on the east and west, and on the north and south. The storms of periodic persecution had scattered this nomadic people all about the Mediterranean without dissolving it. With an indestructible vitality, they even multiplied.

Destitute outcasts, they sought a haven, and in every haven they built a hearth, a workshop, a little trading center. With their quiet but tenacious ways, they attracted curiosity which was soon transformed into bonds of interest. They were rather clannish, but their misfortunes found sympathy everywhere. The educated and refined spirits opposed them, but poor folk willingly accepted these kindred poor and ragged souls. Their sober living and reserved speech inspired confidence; thus their religious belief in a single God brought new breath and hope to a generation of unbelievers, who were disgusted with their own idols which were fickle, corrupt, arid, cruel, and vindictive, as though made of the worst of human clay.

Especially in the most dissolute countries, like Egypt and Syria, Judaism had given the imprint of seriousness and dignity to political and social thinking. The moral superiority of the Jews was recognized and appreciated by the ruling class of the Empire until they became aware of qualities in the Jews which were dangerous to them: their lack of ability to dissimulate, and their exhibition of a pride in their idea of the chosen people, which the leaders took to be an unseemly arrogance.

In these first decades of the century, Judaism was at its most powerful both in its spiritual expansion and in the broadening of the mercantile influences of the Jews. The temple at Jerusalem had become a famous sanctuary, with its authority recognized in every part of the known world. The fabulously rich family of Herod was compliant and weak: they had insinuated themselves into all the crevices, intrigues, and crimes of the imperial family so that they felt more at home in Rome than among their own people in Jerusalem. Princes of dynasties in the Asian provinces, which were dependent on Rome, converted to Judaism in order to marry into the wealth of the Herods. Syria was then forming an almost monotheistic official religion which seemed derived from the Mosaic Law.

Augustus and Tiberius damned the propaganda of the Jews in Rome, however, in contrast to the customary treatment of subject peoples, they permitted the Jews the freedom to be masters in their own land. They scrupulously avoided offending the Jews in their religious conscience, their laws, customs, or rites. Claudius had banned all Jews from Rome when his sleep was disturbed by the noise from their shops and taverns in Trastevere, but he continued to give the impression of cherishing and protecting them in Judea. In short, they constituted a borderless oasis of privilege in the Empire, which was only right in that they were undoubtedly the most educated and civilized of the subject people, heirs and bearers of an early ethical and moral tradition.

The flower of feminine grace and refinement, whose perfume attracted emotional dedication better than any intellectual argument, also bloomed in the Jewish culture. At Syria's capitol, Damascus, which probably outdid all other cities in its degenerate idolatry, almost all the women cloaked their heads in a veil and longed to imitate the ways of freedom and the appearance of the Jewish women.

There is an interesting tale about the royal house of Adiabene, a city on the Tigris river. Ananias, a Jewish merchant, had gone to that city from Jerusalem to trade in cloth, spices, and trinkets. He first gained entry to the harem of the king, where his merchandise was sure to find a ready market. While selling his wares, he mingled flattering words with his trade, and the women listened to his many tales of Jerusalem. Before

33

his stay was over he converted to Judaism all those women in the harem who longed for liberty in any form. Upon hearing this, King Izate asked to hear his words and he too was converted, along with his brother, Monobaze, and his mother, Helen. Izate was so grateful to the merchant that he heaped gifts and thanks upon him. He retained him in the royal palace as counselor and teacher, and the king himself became a zealous observer of the Law. This Ananias, to whom historic legend does not give more detailed countenance, must have been a truly wise and holy man.

Because the Jewish law set forth the practice of circumcision, Izate wanted to undergo the rite which, to one of his years, would be a most harrowing experience. Ananias tried to persuade him that there was no real need for it. Then Eleazar, another merchant who was a more rigid perceptor, agreed to perform the operation. However, the king's mother, Helen, outdid her son in her dedication to the faith and to the Mosiac Law. In her late years, she left the kingdom, in order that she might die in Jerusalem. In order to live in useful works and be able to die in peace, she built a great palace and a mausoleum there. When plague and famine came to the city, she was providence itself for the starving and dying masses. Izate also sent food and money to Jerusalem on this occasion. His sons went to Jerusalem to study the Law, the language, and the customs. However, that worthy family had converted to a Judasim which was, at that time and place, already well on the road to Christianity.

In the meantime, the twelve apostles were opening this new road to Christianity with the tenacity and patience of those who await the sap of the young tree. This new code had grown beyond the most fervent hope of its first followers, and the mission was a consequence and outgrowth of the first rapid expansion. This could only be God's work since the results achieved were extraordinarily superior to the means employed, which gave their preaching an aura of the supernatural.

Five thousand members gained in a few years may not seem to be many, but considering the sparse means and complete lack of authority of these first preachers, they were a phenomenal gain. If the authority of a Joseph of Arimathea, a Nicodemus, or a gifted, wise, and much heeded Gamaliel had been added to the faith of the twelve and their money added to the impecuniousness of the apostles, they most certainly could have accomplished more. It is probable that they did aid the followers of Jesus by protecting and providing for them, since they were finally to suffer persecution and reprisal also. However, they did not place themselves in the forefront of the new movement. They watched the little legion march, compactly and rhythmically, toward an unknown goal, and it seems certain that they took no active part. Perhaps, if they had done so, they would not have obtained the results that the apostles achieved without money or power: they might even have served to attract dangers which the poor and unobstrusive disciples knew how to avoid in those first years.

But five thousand was almost too much, and Jerusalem had no more room within its narrow circle of suspicion and priestly surveillance. Only outside Jerusalem could this five thousand grow to fifty thousand; therefore, it was necessary for the Good News to be carried beyond Jerusalem. And it was also necessary to seek elsewhere for those resources which were no longer available in Jerusalem, where the first community was based on indigence. The church of the new faith threatened to become an asylum of beggars: it was now necessary to add action to prayer and meditation.

Three of the first twelve remained in Jerusalem: Peter, and the sons of Zebedee: these three were the only ones chosen by Jesus to be present at His miracles, the only ones to be near Him in the great mystery of the hours of the transfiguration and on the field of Gethsemane. The other James, a cousin of Jesus known as James the Less, although he was the oldest of the twelve and the only one of them who could be considered an old man, also stayed in Jerusalem. The others took up the pack and mantle of the pilgrim: they placed the few relics of the Gospel in their pack and went on their way. Perhaps young Lazarus went too, and also perhaps his sisters, Mary and Martha, along with other nameless ones.

For the building of the new edifice, stones were brought by anonymous artisans and laborers: they excavated for the construction which none of them would ever see. They knew nothing of one another, and they did not foresee how long that structure would endure, proof against the periodic assaults of earthquake and tempest. Only the real Constructor knows this; they, the workmen, cannot know it. The laborers see only the stone which each one bears on his shoulders, and feel only its weight. They understand that, as one stone is placed on another, the wall rises.

History has lost all trace of them. The known world was confined: a few lands around the Mediterranean, along the Nile and the Euphrates. There were still regions partly unexplored in Gaul, Germany, and Britain, and some islands at the edge of the ocean. But in that small world, the roads had no limits, the deserts were boundless, the mountains almost impassable, and the seas stormy.

The heralds go afoot on those roads, or on camelback: they find people to go with them; they cross plains and deserts where only fierce tribes live; they venture over seas and mountains. They have no other viaticum but their faith, no prospect but martyrdom; their only guide is imitation of the Master. They are as vessels which set sail; the watcher on the shore sees them shrinking on the murky ocean horizon; then he sees them no longer. But he knows that these fishers of men will continue to sail and that they will land on some new shore.

4

Where Did They Go?

Where did they go? If history is like a sun which fixes
men's actions on the screen of time, legend is a moonlit night
where the poetry of fantasy and feeling roams. Just as there
can be no light without shade, so too do we need the firmament as well as the sun.

Where did they go? The Didache, a Christian manual of
the second century, warns: "Wherever the apostle shows himself, he must be received like the Lord, but he is not to remain
in the same place more than one day, or at the most two, and
on leaving he may not receive money but only the food necessary for his journey." A severe precept this: it permits the
apostle no rest in his superhuman labors. This was also the
precept Jesus imparted to the first disciples on the day He sent
them on their first journey.

Andrew, Peter's younger brother, took the road north. He
crossed Samaria, Galilee, Syria, and Cappadocia, and reached
the shore of the Black Sea. He traveled around it and penetrated into Scythia. These were unexplored barbarian lands,

known as "lands of the countries of cannibals." Then he went down into the civilized countries of Macedonia and the Peloponnesian peninsula.

The fisherman of Bethsaida was a man as calm and grave as his older brother was restless and impetuous. He had never called attention to himself in the group around Jesus because he never felt it necessary; the strength of his common sense called attention to him anyway. At difficult moments, the comrades asked his advice, as when they had been faced with the problem of appeasing the hunger of a multitude of followers and had only a few loaves of bread and a few fishes in their packs.

He had been the first to discover Jesus at the ford of Betharabah and he may have been the first to die for Him. How many young men were to follow him: what travail did he suffer? At Patras it was said that he was seen nailed to a cross. Aegeas, the governor of the city, had condemned him to death, and the prayers of the people, led by the governor's own brother, were not enough to liberate him. The cross to which he was nailed was said to be X-shaped, and was called Saint Andrew's cross thereafter in his memory. A merciful Samaritan woman asked for the remains of the apostle, and she buried him.

Philip, the third fisherman from Bethsaida, shy, timid, solitary Philip, also crossed Asia Minor and the Black Sea. After the Master's death, he displayed an unsuspected combative spirit, and he dedicated his ingenuity above all else to smoothing the way for those who were to follow, battling against the bestial pagan cults which were obstacles in the path of the advance of the new faith. He demolished old structures so that others could rebuild on their ruins. He preached against the cult of Mars in Scythia, and against the snake cult in Hierapolis.

39

He was said to have been seen waging the battle for the good for twenty years. He was said to have been heard preaching the Good News in an eloquent manner at Athens before an audience of three hundred philosophers. He was even said to have been seen at Carthage.

The man who had asked the Master to let him see God went in search of God himself in the godless lands, where God always is. No one was found who said he had seen his death. Perhaps he died in bed in a natural way. Perhaps he too was crucified at an advanced age in Emperor Domitian's time. In his pilgrimages, he was often accompanied by his sister, Marian.

John's older brother, James, the great apostle, strong, proud, and audacious, the "Son of Thunder," who one day wanted to set fire to an unfriendly village, stayed in Jerusalem with his brother, Peter, and James the Less. Golden-winged legend took him one day and flew him across the Mediterranean as far as the columns of Hercules. He sowed the seed in Spain, and in Galicia there germinated a special cult in his name from that seed. But history then reclaims James for its own, leads him back to Jerusalem, where he was beheaded about the year 42 A.D.

Nathanael Bartholomew was the handsome, prosperous, young man among the group of hard-working laborers—Bartholomew, the son of the plow; Nathanael, the gift of God. The son of the plough had inherited goods and land from his father; the gift of God dispensed to his companions the gay and pleasing nature bestowed on him by God. Jesus, seeing him beneath the fig tree from afar, had recognized him as an Israelite without guile, and the young enthusiast became a guileless Nazarene, open-hearted and incisive in the fervor of his preaching.

40

He traveled the world over. Like Andrew and Philip, he too started out on the roads to the north, which must have been the traditional roads. Then he turned toward the Orient, went back south, and reached the Red Sea at Aden. He penetrated into the land of the Parthians, into Armenia, and into India. The legend which saw the young man grow old dictated as follows for history: "In greater Armenia, Bartholomew led King Polimius and his wife and all the population of the twelve cities into the faith of Christ; but so many and such illustrious conversions aroused the envy of the priests of other religions, and they incited the King's brother, Astiage, against Polimius. Astiage ordered Bartholomew captured and flayed alive, then beheaded after removing his skin." Legend ventures into the horrible and the macabre; it is tinged with the bloodiest of colors. But history is not less so.

When Thomas, the doubter for love, found the certainty he was seeking, he went forward without ever looking back. A naturally melancholy soul, he made his melancholy a most subtle and penetrating method of communication.

Who was Thomas, what was his life before he was received into the company of the apostles? The doubter for love wanders in a half-light of poetic twilight. Some say that he was a man of art and craftsmanship, an architect who built stately synagogues and houses. Others say that he was a poor lad, who was perhaps an orphan, and that this was the cause of his melancholy, which made him a fervent and persuasive evangelist. "Lord, we know not whither Thou goeth?" he had once said to the Master: now he knew that the Master traveled all roads, and on every road Thomas followed Him, invisible and omnipresent as our own conscience. One has to have once doubted to achieve such perfect certainty.

Thomas crossed all the lands of the Levant. He preached in the lands of the Medes and Persians, of the Ircanians and the

Bactrians. He may have reached Tibet and breached her mountains. Perhaps he even saw the shores of the boundless Pacific.

The tax collector, Matthew, may have stayed with the four major apostles longer than the others. He had left the customshouse at Capharnaum on the first day he felt the call to follow Jesus, but he kept money in reserve and, if he was not the treasurer (an office assigned at the time to others), he may have been the financier of the community for some time.

He spent the first years in the environs of Jerusalem; he retraced the itinerary of the Good News in reverse, from Calvary to Gennesaret. He wanted to revisit the scenes of his happiest days. He wept in search of those who had known Jesus before him. He climbed the mountain of Capharnaum to ask the echoes of the night to bring back that divine voice he had heard there. "Blessed are they that have suffered persecution for the sake of justness . . . Blessed are the poor in spirit . . . Blessed are the merciful . . . Blessed are the peacemakers . . . But woe unto the rich . . . Woe to you, ye that laugh now. . . ."

He had recorded those wondrous words, now he went back over his notes and rearranged them in accordance with his own memories and those of the others. In the still evident traces of the steps of Jesus, he found the pronouncements and images of Him divine. Being a wealthy man, he had been struck above all by the exhortations to poverty by Jesus. These words had shaped his life and he put them into the account he had been writing for others. It was the duty of the disciples to live in poverty as the Master had taught them: "Ask and it shall be given unto you," "Carry neither gold nor silver nor copper money in your belt," "Lay not up for yourselves the treasures on earth, where moth and rust consume. . . ." Freely they must give, as they freely received.

Then Matthew, too, left the land of Israel. He journeyed into Arabia and Persia. He was said to have been devoured by man-eaters. Or beheaded. Or burned alive. He crossed the desert and the Red Sea, and sojourned in Ethiopia beyond the boundaries of the lions. There is a legend which makes him perform the miracle of resuscitating the maiden daughter of the king of Ethiopia, with the result that the king, the royal family, and the entire populace were converted to the new faith. But when the apostle opposed the brother of the converted king in his plan to wed Iphigenia, the resurrected virgin who was dedicated to God, the brother, Atarco, had the apostle spitted on a sword while he knelt at prayer. Legend then takes the Gospel from the hands of the dead Matthew and transfers it to Nathanael, who bore it to the faraway lands of India.

Jude, or Judas Thaddeus, and Simon the Zealot were also cousins of Jesus and perhaps were also the brothers of James the Less. As pale shadows, they hover in the dim unknown.

Was Jude the young husband of the wedding at Cana? Did Jesus perform his first and happiest miracle, that of changing the springs of water into wine, to enliven the wedding banquet? Jude was a courageous man, but the outlines of his deeds are obscured by a gray twilight. A farmer in the company of fishermen and artisans, the things that stayed in his stubborn peasant brain were the invective and admonitions of his great Cousin, and he shouted them from the rooftops in his harsh voice. He, too, journeyed over all the roads the brethren traveled, in Samaria, Idumea, Syria, Mesopotania, and Persia, but the winds of the desert cover his footsteps with sand. He met his brother Simon in Persia; together they joined in battles against the sorcerers Zaroes and Arfatax, and together they were martyred in Beirut.

But legends are like winds that never rest, changing direction at every moment. Another light wind rises to take Jude from that martyrdom and bring him back to Jerusalem where he is granted a long life. But there is no wind which isolates Jesus' younger cousin and shapes him into an attractive and expressive figure. Simon the unknown, was still almost a child among the twelve. The intransigence of his youth made him a zealot, and his preaching regarding the Kingdom of Heaven was said to be the most earthly and expedient of all.

His immovable character gave him the right to succeed his older brother James as head of the church in Jerusalem, and he is borne to that high office by the wind which takes him away from the martyrdom of Beirut. According to legend, he will die a centegenarian in the early part of the second century, in the reign of Trajan. He will die on the cross, like his Master, says one legend; while another one, more gloomy, predicts that he will be quartered.

And the winds scatter the pollen over the expectant earth as the lethargy of winter awaits the blessing of spring. All the weeds of superstition and idolatry are heaped upon the earth; and the rising waters of love sweep away the cesspools of corruption and vice. No one knows the source of these winds, because the sky over the Roman Empire is heavy with clouds and mist, and is shot with blinding bolts of lightning. The horizons are closed but one can note a nearly invisible movement in the air. No one sees or touches the invisible pollen, but a new warmth, a new tremor, a secret and unrestrainable need to open up and receive these words of pollen can be felt. The community of men feels an indistinct anxiety in the deepest viscera for fertilization: a new life stirs in its very lap.

Today is only yesterday's tomorrow, and yesterday is already remote. Only the space of one night lies between them but it seems as though it were the sleep of centuries. No one knows what is said by the voices that pass and pass again in the air, but even the most ineffable sound is on the verge of becoming comprehensible. Those voices speak of human solidarity against the organized selfishness of the state: they speak of liberation from the labor of slavery, of shared goods, of equal rights, of the joy of poverty and the shame of riches, of mercy, charity and forgiveness, of love of one's neighbor as oneself, of the mourners who will be comforted, of the persecuted who will be blessed, of the rich who will not enter the Kingdom of Heaven, of the pure in heart who alone will see God.

And history will then take the flower of legend and make it into the fruit of civilization.

5

The Martyrdom of Stephen

The perfection of the idyll is as of short duration in history as it is in the individual's life, but it brings the benefits inherent to its brevity. If it lasted it would end by exhausting the world's spiritual forces in a kind of numbness and indifference: it is drama which gives these forces action and vigor.

The drama followed quickly on the idyll of the new religion. The growth of the new group, which still had all of the appearance of a sect of political conspiritors, could not long escape the eyes of legal authority. Also, the internal disturbances, which were avoided but not eliminated by the election of the deacons, aroused the suspicions and accusations of the synod.

The proselytes of the new group were in a large part Greek, rather than native-born Jews, and the rigid custodians of the law were particularly intolerant of these intruders, once their actions were apparent. The Diaspora brought back to Jerusalem more people than had left it, and because of this mingling by intermarriage, the purity of the Hebrew people was being vitiated, in the opinion of the authorities. It was, therefore, necessary to uphold the Law, to apply it severely, since this Law was the stronghold of the Jews against aggression from outside and dangers from within. For, although it is seemingly contradictory, it is actually not; the Jew found sympathy everywhere for his mores, but politically he always made enemies and found it necessary always to be on guard against them.

The proselytes were of two kinds: wholehearted proselytes of the sanctuary who observed all precepts of the Law, including circumcision and who were freely admitted to the synagogue; and the proselytes of the gate, those who feared God and who therefore remained at the doorway to Israel. They professed a faith in one God and observed the Sabbath, but they did not submit to the observance of ritual or to the practice of circumcision.

But both groups furnished a more malleable clay than the stubborn natives for those shapers of souls who were the apostles. The Jew of Jerusalem, be he skeptical Sadducee or picky Pharisee, was resistant to new ideas, and either mocked them or was arrogant toward them, while the Hellenistic proselyte, drawn to marvels and ever curious about new things, was easily introduced to the new religion. It was logical that the synod scented the new danger particularly through the attitudes of the latter.

The ostentation of poverty, the joy of poverty, the pride and the boasts of being poor proved humiliating and offensive to the synod. The presence of the beggar who no longer begged because he found another beggar to assist him was becoming intolerable to those rulers whose avidity and imposition of taxes approached the ultimate. The contrast between the ostentatious luxury of the magnates and the extreme indigence of the pariahs of Jerusalem was a spectacle which roused the spirit far more than direct evangelism.

It was rumored that the sins of the rulers in gluttony were no less provocative than their splendor and stubbornness. And, away from the table, there were said to be corruptions even more disgusting. The decadent tolerance of Rome contributed to this situation. The rigid Pilate had been dismissed and the Governor, Vitellius, sent a more conciliating and compromising man, Marcellus, in his place. This was in accord with directives from Rome which tended toward an ever more yielding policy in Palestine, until finally Caligula re-established the dispossessed sons of Herod on the throne, restoring their kingship.

For the past two years, the synod had closed its eyes to the revolutionary aspirations of these twelve men, whom they considered senseless, who had no leader and were followed by a mere train of ragamuffins: now, alarmed, the synod's eyes were suddenly opened. It had heard the gossip of miracles performed by one of them, and this in itself was inadmissable. Such loose talk of miracles had made a Messiah of that simple Galilean Prophet, and such a scandal must not be repeated.

They heard of two incidents which could be considered crimes and which ought therefore to be punished. The leaders of the new congregation demanded that their adherents give up all property to a common fund; and two of those deluded followers, a well-to-do husband and wife named Ananias and Sapphira, had sold their belongings, but had secretly held back a little something for themselves.

Such action was, after all, an innocent lie, a prudent caution rather than a deliberate mockery. If only they had never done so! Peter, the head of the congregation, the fisherman who cured cripples and committed similar outrages, had publicly shamed them with their lie, invoking the fulminations of heaven on them, and the heavens struck them, first the husband and then the wife. Consequently, the crowd around the miracleworker grew, since fear serves as well as love in the inspiration of faith. The crowds brought the sick, the crippled, and the possessed. They put their pallets in the middle of the street in order to lie in his path so that he might cure them with his passing shadow as he walked through the streets.

Whether this tale be truth or fantasy, or a combination of the two (and it is believable that ignorant, idle gossip exaggerated and muddied the event, corrupting Peter's indulgent humanity with vindictive animus), it was repeated to the synod, and they decided that the people must be restrained from this talk of miracles.

Before resorting to force, Caiaphas convened the aging priests, and together they decided to seize the new preachers, not to accuse them as yet, but in order to attempt to persuade them to keep silent and return to work. Rather than force them to come before the synod, they invited them to explain, but the results were negative, since their hidden cunning was of no more persuasion than open violence.

Peter and John replied for the group that they would continue to preach as before but with increasing frequency, since this was their mission and their faith. As usual, Peter was the more quick-tongued. Rather than justify himself and promise obedience, he turned on the priests and accused them of the crucifixion of Jesus. He added that He was not dead, because He was God, Who had ordered them, His disciples, to spread the word of His kingdom throughout the world. Thus, for love of Him, they faced the persecutions and torments He had suffered to redeem mankind.

It was politically prudent not to arouse these arrogant men, who were vowed to sacrifice, and the synod decided to make believe they had not heard these sacrilegious words, which in themselves, demanded punishment. They allowed them to go free, hoping to be able to disarm them by constant surveillance, if they could not bend them with their cunning. But the disciples returned as if to battle, the more incensed and the more ardent. Their propagation of new doctrines, which had first wormed its way secretly into the meetings in hospitable houses or on the solitude of the open road, now openly invaded the temple where beggars and merchants, scribes and women thronged. Since the synod had already identified them and knew what they were about, there was no further reason to remain undercover. They had survived the first test: here they were again, emboldened in their preaching. And the crowd which followed them became more curious and more attentive.

The synod imprisoned them again, this time under lock and key, but some astonishing developments came to pass. The doctrines of the new faith, the new freedom, had infiltrated among the servants, the soldiers, and the jailers, all people committed to obedience who are always the most ready to disobey.

The priests hoped to sleep soundly that night, but they were wakened from a sound sleep by bearers of bad news. The prisoners had escaped. No one knew how they had managed to escape, but the fact remained that they were no longer imprisoned, although the gates were closed and the guards remained at their posts, unharmed. The Angel of the Lord had opened and closed the doors! The Angel of the Lord had freed their prisoners!

Behold, their voices, which everyone by now recognized, resounded under Solomon's porch again, and the great walls of the temple echoed their challenges.

Taken to the council, Peter answered them: "The God of our fathers hath raised Jesus, Whom ye did kill, hanging Him upon a tree; Him God hath exalted with His right hand to be the Creator of salvation, in order to grant Israel repentance and forgiveness of sins; and we are witnesses."

More than anything else, this insistent harping on the sad Passover must have been unpleasant for the priests. They hoped that time would bury their crime, a crime like so many others, one imposed by the public welfare. But the crime rose up, threatening and unsuppressed, to add to the promptings of their own consciences. It rose up in life. Must they then kill the words in the mouths of the vociferators, as they had already done with their Master? Does a new crime erase an old one?

Then a man who was respected and heeded by all rose to speak in the assembly. This was Gamaliel, the most gifted of the doctors of law, the teacher of the young.

He reminded the priests of the recent and past facts of Israel's history, he recounted the history of the plots and revolts which had bloodied their country. From the day the Romans first took power, there had been only blood and desolation. First Theudas had tried to rebel with four hundred men, and four hundred were the victims killed by the imperial cavalry. Then there was Judas of Gamala, the Galilean who had tried to rouse the people against the heavy taxes at the time of Quirinus' census, but he was killed and his followers dispersed. The wise Gamaliel added, "And now I say to you: don't touch these men. If their work and what they preach is of mortal origin, it will be undone. If it comes from God, you cannot undo it." This head of the advanced school attached to the temple was the nephew and disciple of Hillel. From his relative and teacher, he had imbibed a seemingly colorless but deeply persuasive form of argument. Reason and feeling inclined him toward the poor Nazarenes, charitable to men although tenacious in their ideas. Perhaps he sensed some future in those ideas.

The judges accepted Gamaliel's judgment: they released the prisoners though not before belaboring their backs with an energetic thrashing.

But those thirty-nine strokes of the rod were truly beneficial to the spirit of the apostles; they desired them. When the sores of the body had healed they felt happier and lighter. Until now they had suffered no real pain for love of Jesus. Poor, voluntarily poor, and pure in heart; afflicted, but not persecuted. Until now the road had been smooth and free of nails. They had not suffered a tithe of the atrocious pains suffered by Jesus. They were not yet blessed. Now the divine martyrdom began for them too, and the expectation filled them with joy.

The first martyr was Stephen.

This young man, who had not known Jesus, was the first to die for Jesus. A Hellenite Jew, he may have come to Jerusalem to study only a short time earlier. He stood out immediately because of his ardent words and strict actions.

He asked to join the Nazarenes in order to learn their Master's doctrine, and he became an inspired exponent of that doctrine. Peter and the other leaders had quickly realized what an acquisition this great souled youth would be, and they had elected him to the college of the seven deacons. From the first, he found an antagonist in the other youth his own age, a schoolmate who, like him, had returned from the Diaspora, Saul of Taursus, in Cilicia.

In the Synagogue of the Freedmen where Stephen usually preached most successfully, Saul followed him to contradict him, jealous of the influence his rival was gaining. The divine words the Master was wont to say about the instability of the temple, repeating them from the words of Isaias the prophet— that God does not live in houses built by the hands of man— were repeated so insistently by Stephen that they were almost an assault on the temple. This was the surest and most direct way to hurt the priests in their religious and business interests.

The repetition of these words were his death sentence. Once before, overcome by the number and impetus of the new believers, the synod had been forced to permit a debate on the temple steps between the High Priest Caiaphas and James the Less who, because of his age and relationship to Jesus, was already considered the head of the community although no formal hierarchy had been established. Both sides used their most eloquent orators, and the discussion seemed to be going in favor of the Nazarene when Saul rushed into the group, arousing a tumult which put an end to the debate without any conclusion. Someone said he had seen the furious Saul throw himself on James and almost club him, but that the reverence of the others had saved him. Now, in Stephen, they singled out the man who would pay for the guilt of all. They caught him one day when he was defenseless, perhaps tired after a long speech: they attacked him and chased him outside the city with blows and insults, following him with a hail of stones.

There was no trial. The sentence to stoning was the crowd's own decision, incited by Saul. They took off their outer clothes to free themselves for movement in their cruel and happy sport and deposited them at the feet of the instigator, who stood apart, directing the game from afar.

Now the rival was master of the field. The only man of equal stature in terms of devotion and doctrine had disappeared from the scene. The restless and fanatic Tarsian was born with

53

a genius for leadership; he could not accept a lesser position nor tolerate opposition. Fearfully Gamaliel had watched him excel in school: Gamaliel was tolerant and indulgent, Saul extremely intolerant. Among the most intransigent Pharisees, he wanted to be the immovable one.

Men who are destined for great creative roles often go through a malignant fever of destruction between the ages of twenty and thirty. They are ambitious to build on ruins. After Stephen's torment, Saul left his victim under a heap of stones and became the leader of a crusade against the Nazarenes.

Stephen was mourned and buried with religious rites. His companions of the faith were obliged to remain hidden since the days after riots and tortures were always troubled; but the Jews themselves, the proselytes and proselytes of the gate, drew the martyred body from the heap of stones and gave it an undisturbed burial. The beauty of youth touches the most hardened spirits, and certainly there were also pious women who wept over the tomb of this young martyr.

Saul decreed the extermination of the new sect which he considered more dangerous to Israel than those of Theudas and Judas the Galilean. Because the leaders were already coming out of their hiding places to flee, they had to be followed and brought out into the open. He asked the synod to give him credentials and went toward Damascus where Peter was said to be hiding. He was the first who should have been obliged to reason.

Peter had not sought shelter at Damascus. He and many followers who fled with him from Jerusalem had found refuge nearby, in order to be able to return as soon as the storm died down. It would seem that he found temporary asylum at Jericho, where he was reached by a letter from Gamaliel, informing him that Saul was seeking him at Damascus.

6

Simon Magus and the Deacon Philip

In those days the art of prophecy had sprung up again in Palestine. It had never completely disappeared but, overwhelmed by doctrinaire Pharisaism, it had lost its old standing. When lawyers are in power and the public regards them highly, neither prophets nor poets are apt to find followers.

Scribes and priests were drawn by their office to give great importance to sacrifice, which had been neglected by the great prophets of old. The denouncement of sacrifice by Isaias was famous: "To what purpose do you offer me the multitude of your victims, saith the Lord. I am full, I desire not holocausts of rams, and fat of fatlings, and blood of calves, and lambs, and buck goats." And Jesus had said that God wants mercy, not sacrifice.

Now the new religion, born of Christ's announcement of the Good News, could not but hold the prophets in great esteem, and on the scale of grace the gift of prophecy ranked second after that of the apostolate in the dogma and hierarchy which were in the process of formation. Doctors of the Law were relegated to third place. But in every age there are true and false prophets, and the false especially abounded in Palestine, a fertile ground which poverty rendered particularly responsive to fakery. Misery makes people gullible and encourages the exploiters of that credulity in every sort of hocus-pocus. In every part of Palestine the famine predicted by Joseph's dream of the starved cattle seemed to reappear.

The persecution which followed the martyrdom of Stephen had driven the disciples from Jerusalem. They found an unexpected field of action outside the city. Until now their work had been one of persuasion, not difficult among people disposed to be persuaded. Now they found their first obstacles which had to be demolished patiently.

The bread of false prophets and false healers was a worse enemy than the physical persecutor since it upset the theory of their work. An imitator and corruptor of the Gospel was considerably more dangerous than an openly hostile priest, so that their flight from Jerusalem became the beginning of a mission. It can also be said of the new faith that every soaring flight rises from a fall and that at the beginning of a great truth there is almost always a small error. Samaria especially had always spawned many of the false prophets, and in those days Simon of Gitton, a healer and wonderworker, was much heeded, adored like a god by the rabble. At first there were two, Simon and Dositheus, who proclaimed themselves disciples of John the Baptist; in fact, Dositheus, who was the older and the teacher of Simon, presented himself as the Messiah whom Moses had announced for the end of time, and his followers believed they saw him borne off to heaven like Moses and Elijah. But Dositheus disappeared quickly, and Simon of Gitton remained to unhinge the superstitious Samaritans.

Simon had heard of the words and works of Jesus, and being a man of talent as well as ambition, he did not find it hard to consider himself Jesus' rival. He had studied in Alexandria, equipping himself with a hodgepodge education in which occultism, Buddhism, and pantheism were mingled in an extravagant system of synthetic philosophy. An extravagant mind spoiled by unhealthy license, he amused himself by tinkering with a game of magic symbols and fantastic allegories which resembled the Good News as much as the mud puddle and the mire resemble the clear water of a spring. He claimed that his wife Helen represented the supreme intelligence, that in her first incarnation she was Helen of Troy. She was a prostitute in Tyre when Simon met her, and the "Great Power" in him redeemed her, and he made her his bride. A histrionic parody of Magdalen!

Simon wanted a position of power for himself in the new group, but an autonomous and lofty one, not as a follower of Jesus, but as an equal. He said he was in mystic communion with the Son of Man. With Jesus he had suffered in the flesh; he had been crowned with thorns and nailed to the cross along with Jesus. He was Jesus himself. The credulous Samaritans, enthralled by the cascades of words and the mumbo-jumbo, adored Simon Magus as a being superior to every angel, power, and virtue. It was necessary to root out the weed of spurious perversion, and so deacon Philip was sent to Samaria.

Philip was a prophet, the father of four girls who were also endowed with the gift of prophecy. He worked miracles too, especially in healing the sick, and above all he possessed the rare gift of plain persuasive speaking. For this reason he had been chosen. He had achieved great success in Samaria's capital, Sebastye, by speaking in the synagogues and healing the sick. He founded a little community of Nazarenes there, who had been baptized by him in the name of Jesus. Simon went to hear him and realized that he must make him a friend and colleague if he were to dominate him later with his own theatricality. In the beginning he asked to be baptized in the name of Jesus Christ, and Philip baptized him. He also asked to receive the Holy Spirit, but this Philip could not give, since that gift was reserved to the apostles.

About this time, the chief apostles, Peter and John, had received word of Philip's success in Samaria, and they arrived at Sebastye to complete the deacon's work. Then the episode occurred which was to mark the beginning of the heresies in the heart of growing Christianity. Simon asked Peter to impart to him too the powers of prophecy and miracle-working and, since he had acquired great riches with his magic arts, he offered the apostle money. Peter rejected the money, cursed the merchant of holiness, and asked God to pardon that which he found unpardonable, recommending Simon's soul to the Almighty.

The humiliated blusterer did not surrender. Was Peter led astray by his native ardor? Might he perhaps have obtained the rebel's submission and converted this powerful heretic into a disciple in action if he had relied on the divine law of pardon taught him by Jesus? In the long course of religion, it had happened before and will happen again that the haughtiest of adversaries has been transformed into an obedient supporter, active and trustworthy.

Simon was a man of great energy, and he continued to sway the crowds of pagans in Syria, in Asia, and perhaps also in Rome. Among his followers were Menander of Cepharethea and Cleobius. He founded a church in Antioch. But he lacked the depth to add moral example to action, and his ethical system was too corrupted by licentious ways and lewd magic, the bonds of the period, to be able to conquer souls which longed to be freed of those bonds.

Philip continued his preaching in Samaria. He became one of the most assiduous heralds of the Gospels of Jesus. He was also called by the name evangelist as were those who had actually heard the Gospel from Jesus and who had written it down. His four prophetess daughters followed him. It was most charming to see this family of inspired maidens under the guidance of a still young, indefatigable father, journeying from village to village. There were other such united families, composed and harmonious, and one of the fruits of the newborn religion was this spiritual concord which grew within families, becoming a work of persuasion to the outer world.

From Samaria, Philip was inspired to move south, a terrain which was still to be plowed. He left Jerusalem behind and set out across the sandy desert along the shore route to Gaza, the country of the Philistines. Before he reached the city, he had an encounter which was to mark a fork in the path of Christianity, which had been, until then, straight and without crossroads. An Ethiopian of great power, Queen Candace's eunuch and supervisor of all the treasures in the realm, was returning to Ethiopia from Jerusalem after completing his ritualistic devotion in the temple. He was traveling in a royal coach, and to occupy himself during the long journey, he read the book of the prophet Isaias.

His curiosity aroused, Philip followed him, and they found themselves seated together at the same dinner table at a stopping place. They exchanged a few words about the sacred book which Philip had been astonished to see in the hands of a pagan. They continued the journey together because the eunuch asked his chance companion to be seated next to him in his coach. He was reading the book acquired in Jerusalem as a man reads ancient inscriptions in a language he doesn't know, trying to decipher it without grasping the deep poetic and prophetic sense it has. He asked Philip to explain it to him, and Philip explained that the ancient prophet foretold the coming of the Messiah in that chapter. Now the prophecy had been fulfilled: the Messiah had come; He was named Jesus and He was a native of Nazareth. And, as the prophet had foretold, He had been oppressed, afflicted, and killed.

Philip then told the Ethiopian the story of Jesus' life and of His death and Resurrection. He also spoke of the way man might follow Jesus to the Kingdom of God, a way of virtue and sacrifice, which began with baptism and could lead to supreme martyrdom. Talking and meditating, they rode along side a small stream whose limpid green waters gurgled in the shadow of the sycamores. The Ethiopian could not understand the real significance of the Messiah, but he had a mystic tendency and he perceived a confused impression of the beatitudinous aura around Jesus.

Moved by the evangelist's words, he stopped the coach and asked his new friend to baptize him in the brook if he thought him worthy of it. Philip waded into the water with him and baptized him. The Ethiopian was not a Jew, he was not circumcized, he was perhaps only a proselyte of the gate to whom baptism could not be granted. It was the first opening to the limitless world of the Gentiles.

The newly baptized Ethiopian continued on his way, no doubt anxious to tell Queen Candace of his great adventure. Philip was both uplifted and dismayed by his daring and unusual action, which he had performed on impulse, but at the unknown bidding from the Highest, without realizing what consequences the act might have, nor could he imagine how his superiors would receive it. In this state of exaltation and dismay he felt himself raised into the air and wafted to the city of Azotus, on the edge of the more immense desert. He continued his preaching to the caravans of the Orient here. From Azotus he went up beside the sea to Joppa, turned inland at Lydda and reached the sea again at Caesarea, founding a tiny church in every city where he stopped.

Marvelous results were achieved by deacon Philip in these first years of the new faith's expansion. He and his daughters took up residence at Caesarea and the church he founded there became a great one. Caesarea was Christianity's first seaport.

7

Saul—The Man
of Thwarted Ambition

The chief threat to the apostles—present at almost every moment in almost every spot—the most fearful enemy, was young Saul.

The priests of the temple were for the most part wealthy, old men, lovers of quiet living. They watched over the new movements and tried to lull and deflect their influence without resorting to open hostilities. As long as their own interests were not touched, they did not bother about ideas. They would not give sovereign importance to the Nazarene preachers, who were so obstinate but so poor, or show fear of them because it would lessen their own importance and authority. They could not admit that someone or something, a man or a sect, could even touch them, let alone destroy them.

Instead this young Jew from Asia fought them in their ideas only, with fervor, intelligence, and indomnitable energy.

He was much more terrifying than old Caiaphas and his slaves and hirelings.

Never had they seen anyone more determined and dedicated to their destruction. In comparison, Judas Iscariot was only misguided—a weakling or a madman. There was complete mental clarity in this young man's enmity. They had never cared for Judas, but they would have admired Saul had he been their friend. Saul was small and younger than they, but they sensed a superior being. They felt the dazzling intellect that dwelt within his graceless, ill-made form: his body seemed sickly, weak, unimpressive except for the large head which was already almost bald. He did not speak easily, his voice was unpleasing, his gestures awkward, but when he chose to say a few words one was impelled to listen, and a curious and astonished silence formed around him. When he appeared among the important men of the synod, he dominated them with his oratory. It was not copious but vehement and lashing. The wrestler had begun by wrestling against himself, and he had conquered all his imperfections.

The mark of predestination was stamped on his aquiline countenance, and under his beetling eyebrows, the deep, piercing eyes flashed with the light of a rebel angel. The youth was born to be a guide and a leader. They felt it, and certainly he felt it too. They felt he was made of the same stuff they were, the stuff of the safest and soundest apostles—Peter, John, and James—but so much more daring and educated. They were ignorant, made eloquent and wise by faith alone, but he had obtained a great deal of culture through long study. There was no doubt that he too was animated by faith and principle, by a dream and a tenacious will to action, but what immoderate ambition, what enormous ideas, what fantasies were nursed in his stormy soul? Was it a hellish or a heavenly fire that burnt in his flaming spirit?

Did he consider himself the heir and emulator of the great rebels, all of whom had ended in defeat and ignominy? Did he also aspire to the fleeting and cursed glory of the mercenary and pervertor whom Jesus had come to deny? And did he persecute the crucified Jesus in His apostles out of a spirit of opposition, a Pharisaical fanatacism, or out of a satanic pride and envy? Was he imbued with the evil spirit of the traitor of Kerioth in a more ardent and aggressive form?

But he was uncorrupted, an honest man, more intransigent with himself than with others. From what they had learned, he lived modestly in his sister's house in Jerusalem, studying and working. His sister carried on the family business of making and selling canvas. He integrated and alternated manual labor with mental occupation, working at his sister's loom and studying at the temple's advanced school. He lived an uncomfortable life between the commotions of the flesh and the raptures of the mind. He loved solitude and had retired into it, but he came rushing out as soon as he heard about a meeting of Nazarenes under Solomon's porch or in the open air outside the city. He seemed sad and gloomy when he was not speaking. There was a thwarted and rebellious look on his cavernous face. When he spoke it was transfigured with prophetic genius.

Born in Tarsus in Cilicia, his family may have come from the city of Giscala in Galilee. He was of the tribe of Benjamin, and for this reason he had been given the name of the first king of that tribe. His family had double citizenship, both Tarsian and Roman, the first giving him the legal right to obtain the second and to establish clearly his Roman citizenship: his father had added the Roman name Paul to his Hebrew name Saul.

Saul was still a boy when he lost his mother, and the mother of Alexander and Rufus, who may have been the wife of the Cyrenian Simon of Calvary, was like a foster mother to him. His father was a well-to-do man, a maker of goat's hair cloth, the coarse, rainproof material called cilice after the region of its origin, used for soldiers' and nomads' tents. Saul's father was a Pharisee of strict observance, and the boy Saul had imbibed his uncompromising nature and love of the study of the Law from him.

Until the age of ten, Jewish boys attended no school except the "vineyard," the school attached to the synagogue: at ten they began to study the Law. Like all unruly and stubborn boys, who seem lazy because they don't apply themselves but easily retain everything they are taught instead, Saul learned the Law's precepts so well that they became a provocation to error. He confessed in old age that he had been introduced to sin at the age of thirteen when he read the commandment which prohibited it. There would be fewer errors, perhaps, if the world had fewer prohibitions.

But while strictly Jewish in the family and in the synagogue, Saul's education was enriched and complemented by the Hellenist influence then flourishing in the university at Tarsus, for Tarsus was not far from Samos and Ephesus and the rich aura of spiritual learning diffused by the two great teachers of those cities some five centuries earlier still emanated from its schools. Thus he was not unacquainted with Ionian philosophy.

At that time the philosopher Athenodorus, who had been the friend and teacher of Augustus, lived in Cilicia's capital, a city almost the equal of the greatest cities of the Orient in size and riches. This gifted teacher, the son of peasants, enthusiastically encouraged learning; and his philosophy, rooted in Platonism, developed in a climate which had something almost Christian about it. These are sayings of his: "Know that you will not be liberated from your passions until you do not want to beseech God for anything you would not feel free to ask of Him in public; Live with men as if God were watching you, and speak with God as if men were listening to you." Seneca had learned the meaning of conscience from Athenodorus: these words of that Roman philosopher come from his Asiatic teacher: "What matter if others do not know that you have done something shameful if you are aware of it?"

With this intellectual and moral background, Saul arrived in Jerusalem at fifteen to study the Talmudic law. Gamaliel immediately selected him from the Hellenist youth, noting his unprepossessing appearance and his haughty and ambitious spirit. He may have thought he had the makings of a successor, a teacher of the Law: he did not think that the founder of a new religion could be made of such stuff. Meanwhile, Paul made himself the fiercest persecutor of that religion.

The best student in school, Saul wanted to be the leading doctor of Law outside the school. The synod had instituted a kind of inquisition against the new sect, and Saul appointed himself its leader.

Young men who feel "superhuman talents" in themselves are inflamed and blinded by flashes of divine madness at the threshold of active life, a divine madness which can last for more than a moment. If it does not become a misguided habit of mind but is transformed into light, it may be beneficial to the spirit; if it accompanies the young men past the threshold and is transformed into smoke, it can produce darkness and imbalance. In that flash the young man of genius feels himself different from the rest: superior, privileged, predestined, unique, made of incorrigible stuff—the others around him are barely shadows, transient and fleeting.

The boy who is becoming a man thinks he was born for some purpose not yet revealed to him, lofty and certain. He imagines himself endowed with faculties and powers which will be explained to him when he has found the way to great conquests. He considers himself a kind of god: then the spite and the revolt of the fallen angel ensue.

Had Saul known Jesus? Had he listened to some of His speeches and parables? Had he been present at His trial? Did he see Jesus die on the Cross? Did the cry of Magdalen: "He is risen! He is risen!," reach his ear? None of the disciples remembered seeing his face among the Pharisees, who were so humiliated and scorned by the Master's invective at the banquet at Simon's house, nor among the merchants chased from the temple, who had been unable to hurl the stones hidden under their tunics. They had not seen him among the furious crowd crying out for the crucifixion of Jesus under Pilate's tribunal.

Perhaps Saul was visiting his family at that time, and neither saw nor heard anything. Perhaps he knew about it and had carefully avoided Jesus' presence because of his envy. He may have heard about Calvary from certain other Tarsians, for Andronicus, Junius, and Herodian had seen the crucifixion and returned to Tarsus much moved by it, even though they were not converted. But Saul shrugged his shoulders. What was the Galilean prophet, the self-proclaimed Messiah, to him? He too was full of ancient wisdom and would have been able to say the same things in different words. He too could sway a crowd and lead them where he would. If a Messiah, a national hero, Savior of the people of Israel, was about to arrive, was he, Saul, unworthy of the role? Who could deny that he was capable of it? Who would refuse him the right to be the catalyst and captain of his people? The author must be permitted to imagine

67

these agitations and these ambitions in Saul's tempestuous soul.

Now they said his great Rival, killed by crucifixion, had risen from the dead. But had He truly risen? He was a shade, a memory, but that shade, that memory, multiplied in thousands of followers who believed in Him, believed in Him as the Son of God. The seed of wheat thrown on the ground had rotted, but rows of green sprang up everywhere from that dissolution. He, Saul, had not been present to crush the seed, but he would scythe the plants before they put forth fruit. Stephen, the most eloquent of the disciples, had been buried under a heap of stones: now the others must be hunted down and disposed of.

The inflexible ascetic was melancholy. His thwarted rebel's soul was gnawed by the bitterness of unachieved heights, heights achieved by others who proclaimed and preached. But he was young, obeyed, feared, and followed. Ambition swelled his heart, and in his head thoughts seethed like a fever. He knew well enough now that he was not the chosen one whom he had glimpsed in that fifteen-year-old's moment of glaring illumination, because his reason had extinguished the fire without leaving the smoke of fanaticism. But he might well be a great prophet and teacher of the Law. Messiah he was not, but there remained to him the duty and the will to give merciless combat to those Nazarenes who worshipped another Messiah. He began his holy crusade in the name of the God of Israel.

Peter and the others were informed by Gamaliel that the infuriated Saul had armed himself like a Roman soldier, taken a handful of zealots even more heavily armed than himself, and gone to Damascus to rout them out. They left their hiding place and returned to Jerusalem. Here they were reached by astounding and unbelievable news: Saul himself had been converted to their faith in Jesus. Had the Master accomplished His greatest miracle from Heaven?

8

Why Do You Persecute Me?

Absolute governments always make the mistake of banishing those they consider dangerous or undesirable. They would serve their purpose better if they kept their adversaries under surveillance and thus weakened and disarmed them, but it is a rare thing to find persecutors who have the minimum of intelligence needed for their trade.

Among all the activities of human reason, political and religious persecution are the most unreasonable because they invariably produce results contrary to their intentions. The idea is to deflate a new sect—a young faith—by dispersal, but the fragments join together wherever they find welcome, and instead of going out, the scattered fire lights new sources of flame all around.

So the Nazarenes, exiled and hunted from Jerusalem, journeyed from land to land in search of asylum, and then transformed every asylum into an altar and pulpit of propaganda. The new faith would not have spread so rapidly if it had been tolerated, or ostensibly ignored, at Jerusalem. For it was not only the leaders who carried it all over the world. History

69

registers only the words and deeds of the protagonists, and the longer arms of legend follow and gather leaves dispersed by the winds; but there are innumerable nameless ones ignored by both history and legend. The painstaking and devoted labor of these unknown workmen truly makes one think of the sacred travail of maternity. Faceless and voiceless to us, they waited for the ideas of others before building, but they had the strength to load themselves with stones for the edifice. Without these obscure workers, the great architects who came afterward would have been unable to construct anything.

The Jews scattered throughout the world had not remained isolated in exile. With their simple needs and sound ways, their abilities in commerce and hard work, they multiplied; and the first individuals united into families, and the families came together into colonies. This has been their strength, which has preserved their individuality and kept them from drying up throughout the most barren centuries.

Alexandria, Antioch, Damascus, Ephesus, and Corinth already had neighborhoods and suburbs which were completely Jewish, with Jewish stores, synagogues, and schools, almost like little states within the greater ones. According to the historian Flavius Josephus, there were enough Jews at Damascus to furnish ten thousand men at arms. A great part of Alexandria was assigned to the Jews as their own domain. But their young men eligible for military service were not obliged to serve because of a special privilege granted by the emperor. Although he usually recruited his provincial legions on the spot, adding Roman soldiers for discipline and security, the Jews were exempted. It was a special concession and precaution at the same time: Jews were not to be trusted.

For these reasons too, the relationships between the Jews and pagans could not be close and cordial. Each one went his own way, and in many cities the two ways were separated by hedges. But curiosity, which is always a stimulus to confidence, can also generate it. The cohesive and secluded Jewish community was becoming a powerful drawing force in a restless and bewildered world which sought something to believe in and to sustain it.

In many Jewish communities there were so many Gentile converts to Judaism mingled with the Jews of Palestinian origin that they became truly amalgamated communities. Where the mingling was most advanced, and they felt and practiced mutual living most sincerely, the advance guards of Nazarene pilgrims found ready entry. They asked for bread, which the Jew never refuses, and paid their hosts by repeating a parable of love learned from the apostles. The beggar slept in the guest bed, and after he had rested, he explained the merits of baptism to the master of the house.

Restless spirits, who held dreams of liberation from the Roman yoke in their inmost hearts, listened with growing hope to these stories of the Messiah who had already arrived to redeem and liberate them. There were other Messianic groups, not founded by Nazarenes, in the process of formation at Damascus and elsewhere, together with pilgrims who called themselves penitents of Israel.

Especially the proselytes and the "fearful of God" were attracted to these gentle, poor, and joyful heralds of the Good News. It was natural that the Gentiles who had taken the first step toward the Mosaic Law were disposed to go further and accept the faith of Jesus. They found the sober and thrifty qualities which had first attracted them to the Sons of Israel in an even simpler and more clear-cut form in these Nazarene Jews. The joy of poverty, the denunciation of the rich for selfishness, the principle that everyone has a right to a simple minimum only and that the rest belongs to the needy were concepts which stirred their hearts, an unheard of language of goodness which did not seem to come from mortals' mouths. And the way of prayer which Jesus had imposed, closed in their houses and in their hearts, was much more meaningful and effective than showy public prayers.

The Jewish beliefs were persuasive because of their inspiring language, but in practice the rigid formalism of their rites was rather annoying. The first refuges had been tolerant and discreet with the proselytes as long as they were guests of their country; once established as businessmen, they made these same proselytes feel rather uncomfortable, binding them between the demands of a favorable profit and loss of balance and the narrow straits of fanaticism.

The proselyte women particularly, who had been easily conquered by the Jews, now gave themselves fearlessly to the new preachers of goodness; for they lived chastely and respected mothers, wives, and widows almost to the point of adoration. In all of Seleucid Asia at this time there was such female licentiousness that women ended up by being considered the scourge and evil genius of mankind. The words of the Gospel were like a cleansing bath to these poor rejected creatures, purifying them of their age-old filth. The first women who had ministered devotedly to Jesus were also ardent priestesses of the new religion.

Where were Mary, her sister Martha, and their brother Lazarus? They had shut themselves up with their memories. But a pious legend sweeps up this family so dear to Jesus, to take them across the Mediterranean and deposit them at Marseilles. Here the legend has them sheltered in a grotto which the popular poetry of the people still calls Magdalen's Grotto. From there they go to Lyons, where a flourishing colony of believers springs up. Flowers of virgins bloom, and martyrs abound who fill the air with celestial perfume. Mary of Magdalen will be born once again in heroic Blandina.

To Magdalen, poetry and art will later give weight and grace almost equal to that of the Mother.

Saul must have felt ill at ease in Jerusalem with his convictions and fantasies of grandeur. It was too small a field for his tumultuous activities; a kingdom of the poor and resigned did not suit the spirit of the arrogant battler. The synod could easily control Jerusalem's intimidated and strictly supervised community, made helpless by extreme poverty, reduced to the status of a territorial militia. For him the struggles in the open field, hand-to-hand combat, hunting down the enemy in its secret haunts—these were exciting and real. He was the foreign legion.

Armed with letters of credential, he moved on to Damascus, a great and rich city, the capital of Syria and the most ancient city in the ancient world, "God's paradise." Though it was not true, he had been told that the adversary to be destroyed had taken refuge there, and he left in chase of Peter. But before he set foot in the city, there befell him that marvelous event which, after the Resurrection of Jesus Christ, was the beginning of the new era in the world.

Saul and his escort of a few youths had already arrived within sight of the city wall. Was he thinking of a brief stop to rest his horse after the gallop alongside the Jordan and Mount Hermon's heights? Or, with throat parched by the hour and season, did he want to quench his own thirst at a spring near the path's edge? Or under the shadow of the great cedars did he wish to gather his thoughts and bend them toward action? What wildness, what storms roiled in his heart, what passionate hallucinations burned his brain, what designs of persecution?

The lightning bolt of illumination struck him unexpectedly, it went through him from his head to his heart, threw him off his horse, and blinded him. They said a sudden storm had broken with thunder and lightning. His eyes did not see what was happening in the heavens and over the earth. His ears heard a voice which pronounced human words, but it was not the voice of man:

"Saul, Saul, why persecutest thou Me?" Saul did not see, but he heard and he could speak. He answered: "Who art Thou, Lord?" The voice, which was not human but was filled with the silence of all things, said: "I am Jesus who thou doth persecute." It spoke again and in the last words it seemed more human. "It is hard for thee to kick against the goad."

Saul spoke too, or he stammered. If in that moment he had had full awareness, perhaps he would not have recognized his own voice; he would have listened to it as one listens to another's voice which bears no resemblance to one's own. And he would have been astounded to hear himself speaking like someone else, to feel himself living like a different person. "What will Thou have me do, Lord?," he asked.

He had never obeyed, he had always commanded: he was accustomed to demanding, not asking. But the new man who was inside him asked and obeyed.

The voice of Jesus raised him from the ground and guided him. "Rise and go into the city. There you will be told what you must do."

The young men of his following heard words come out of his mouth, but they did not understand their meaning or to whom they were addressed, because they were incapable of hearing the arcane voice which spoke to him. They must have thought he was suffering from sunstroke or had taken leave of his senses. They saw him raise himself on all fours, fum-

74

blingly, like a man who is coming out of a dizzy spell, and he looked with unseeing eyes into nothingness.

He was blind. They supported him and took him to the city, where they left him at the home of an acquaintance, a man named Judas. This haughty man who had traveled with them on horseback now continued his journey on foot.

His followers did not know what to do, nor to whom to entrust their leader for treatment; nothing like this had ever happened before. Saul came to his senses, but his sight did not return: he was a different man. He used words other than those they were accustomed to hear him speak. While they were thus perplexed and dismayed, someone named Ananias came to ask about the ailing man. He was a Nazarene newly-arrived at Damascus, a man famous for his healing powers, perhaps one of the first seventy sent to preach by Jesus.

That day, Ananias had also had a vision, and he too had heard a divine voice speak to him. That voice had ordered him to go to the house of Judas on Straight Street, the big street which cut through the city. Here he would find the young Tarsian Saul, who had lost his sight and was now praying. Ananias was to put his hands on him so that Saul might see again. The Nazarene listened to the voice from on high, but he was uncertain in his task because he knew Saul, at least by reputation. He knew that this driven youth was Jesus' most bitter enemy and the most cruel persecutor of His innocent followers. Was he to become the accomplice of the persecutor, and of the priests who had given him so much power? But the voice from Heaven encouraged him to obey the order because the persecutor was no longer a persecutor; in fact, he had been chosen by the Lord for great works and martyrdom.

So Ananias went to visit Saul, who was already expecting

75

him since he had also had a vision of a holy man, who was to have received a divine order to come and lay hands on him and cure him of his sudden blindness. Obediently he kneeled and submitted to the Lord's will and Ananias' rite. He asked the prophet for baptism and let himself be immersed in the purifying water. Little scales, which had nearly closed his eyes, fell from them. The blind man was again able to see.

He had been blind not for three days only but for many years, and he now saw that which he had never seen. He saw all aspects of life and eternity with new eyes. He saw the ways which lead to the truth, the ways of love. The earth and the sky looked different to him from what he had always thought he saw, as mountain peaks are different when seen in their own light than when seen reflected upside down in water. He had truly passed from the shadow into the light.

The others saw a new man too. His own comrades looked at him with annoyed and disappointed surprise; the followers of Ananias looked at him with feeling curiosity, pitying even if unbelieving. Balaam too, in the time of the temples, had heard a voice from the sky order him not to persecute the people of Israel again; and he had put down his arms, reformed, and converted. Was this ancient miracle re-created? Had the hand of God again halted the potent evildoer on his iniquitous path, showing him the road of supreme good?

Now they heard words never before heard from his mouth. They asked him questions; he was quiet and shy, replying more with his glance than with his tongue. When he began to speak, he himself really felt that it was no longer his own voice but that of another speaking from his throat. It had the same firm tone but the spirit was trepidacious. He began to feel as if the being that used to live in his body had gone out of it, the way an old sword comes out of its sheath; and another person, greater, stronger, and bursting with love, had now come to inhabit it. The blazing new sword! No, he was not the Messiah, but the true Messiah was entering into him, and the talent of the persecutor was being transformed into the herald's talent.

He spent three days in Judas' house, humble and obedient. He accepted the care heaped on him, as the convalescent is receptive to the hands of the nursing Sister. He buried himself in books and prayers. Then he dismissed the companions who had followed him from Jerusalem, he thanked his hosts, and went away without telling anyone where he was going or when he would come back.

Not even he knew this. He had neither purpose nor plan in his mind. He went where inspiration led him, until another voice from the sky should tell him where to stop. He went to be alone with himself, with that other self which had arisen in him driving out the first, which grew and strengthened and asked for action. The Lord had withdrawn for forty days, they said, to the Mount of Temptations, before starting His mission: great sinner that he was, he must live in solitude, meditation, and penitence for far longer.

"Become what you are, Saul," he told himself. It was the precept he was to repeat always to his students: become what you are. And he trained himself to become what he was.

He withdrew into the Arabian desert where he had no company except his thoughts. For three years he lived there. He was not seen in Damascus, nor in Jerusalem, nor in his native city of Tarsus during that period. He broke all the strings which bound him to the synod and to his family. He was alone—alone with his remorse and God's pardon.

To meditate and to prepare one's spirit for the new action one still has to live and bread is necessary to the life of the body; and so he came out of his solitude to seek work.

The word of his conversion spread rapidly. On the one

hand it was brought to Jerusalem by Saul's followers, who reported the failure of the Damascus expedition to the High Priest, on the other hand it was told by the Nazarenes, who marveled joyously as they told the apostles of the rout and the repentance of their most fearsome adversary.

Then these tales, of defeat on the one hand and victory on the other, died out. Saul the Tarsian was no longer a topic of conversation—forgotten, disappeared. It had only been an episode of the great struggle. Other marvelous events were taking place in the land of all marvels.

9

Peter and the Centurion

While Saul was preparing the great revolution in the Arabian Desert, deep in prayer, penitence, and meditation; the major disciples returned to Jerusalem. Peter, and James and John, the sons of Salome, and the Lord's cousin James came together again. No more is heard of the other eight, except for voices in the wind.

The thread which united the outposts to the mother country is broken, and now they go where destiny carries them. They have already entered the Kingdom of God. The four remain in Jerusalem, some for a long time, others for less. They become the pillars of the new Church.

They were left in peace. For some months no one bothered or harmed them. Their discretion and the discomfiture of their adversaries contributed to this peace or truce. Uneasy times had come again for Israel's people. The constant pattern of good and evil events which made this people oscillate in a perpetual see-saw of misery and prosperity, freedom and slavery, now veered toward evil.

There had been a period of great favors, privileges, and soft words bestowed by Rome. When the strict Pilate was recalled, the easygoing Marcellus came to replace him, and the Jews' stock rose on the imperial exchange. The legate Petronius protected and defended them. Added to the abundant rains which came to save Palestine from a disastrous drought, there was again some reason to believe that they were, in truth, the chosen people.

Now, with a shift of the political winds, annoyances and impositions returned: this proud people, who became arrogance personified when times were good, made themselves humble and submissive under the oppression of others. They needed a free hand before they could unleash a combative spirit. Caligula had petted them, heaping honors and benefits on the Herods; he had even given them spiritual power in the temple, but he soon went mad, and his madness burst out in all sorts of cruelty and strange jests in Palestine too.

That vile and demented despot would have been a supportable evil if he had not proliferated an unhealthy spawn of more vile and base proconsuls who were not demented. There occurred in the Roman Empire what happens in all regimes which are grasped in the fist of a madman: its officials gave way to every kind of outrage great and small, seasoned with mockery, as permitted by their office. They stretched their imaginations to invent malign tricks which would wound the Jews in what they held most dear—their religion; just as, in other times and places, despots torture and mortify their subjects through their families, their self-respect, and their culture.

If Caligula did not succeed in getting his golden statue put up in the temple, his zealous functionaries demanded that every sacred spot in the country be profaned by busts of Caesar and other imperial emblems. The priest bowed their heads, and their animus against the humble Nazarenes also weakened.

He who is mortified by the strong, does not gladly make the weak pay for his mortification, and so is able to raise his head. In the meantime, he is somewhat servile and abject while he awaits his hour. So the priests and the Pharisees left the Nazarenes in peace; they watched them, but abstained from persecution.

The second reason for the truce was the presence of James the Less. He was becoming more outstanding each day, and finally became the recognized and obeyed leader of the new Church. His relationship to Jesus, his age and physical presence, his calm speech, his fair and cautious, if not profound, wisdom his mature common sense, his measured timing which kept him always midway between the synagogue and the Christian community, between the Mosaic Law and the grace of Jesus, conciliating and diplomatic, these were the qualities which brought him that authority and position. In a group of young disciples (Peter was not more than forty, John less than thirty), he was already old, past seventy. With his flowing Mosaic beard and abundant long hair, he seemed enveloped in a black-and-white mantle; an incarnation of the Old Testament rather than of the Good News.

He had not been one of the first to believe in Jesus, as John had already noted; in fact, he entered rather late into the company of the disciples. His austere inclination was toward the suffering asceticism of the ancient prophets rather than the gladsome teaching of the Galilean. Now, after the death of his divine Relative, he had closed himself within the rigors of meditation and penitence. It was said he never bathed himself with water nor anointed his skin with oil, that he never drank wine—that wine which had always brought joy to Jesus' dinner table—nor ate any animal flesh. In all weather he wore the same coarse woolen tunic. He spent days and nights deep in prayer, and there were callouses on his knees from kneeling on the stones. His asceticism fell into exaggerations for which Jesus would have scolded the Pharisees, and this was one reason why the Pharisees respected him.

The Pharisees respected him, the Saducees a little less so; but neither the one nor the other ever molested him. He had no enemies in any party. A juncture between Judaism and the new faith, he was surrounded by veneration. Everyone called him the bulwark of the people—the just, the wise. If a rash contamination of the ancient with the modern were permissible, he could be called the president of the new religious and social republic, Peter the prime minister and actual strength, and Paul the captain of the army.

Peter was another fervent and active spirit. He threw himself into action with the firstborn's determination, accepting the obligations of his position. No one knew better than he how to recount the deeds and repeat the sayings of the Divine Master. He barely knew how to write and therefore wrote little but, after Pentecost, his tongue was loosed and he spoke freely at every meeting. He was even more persuasive in private conversations, subdued discussions where he could confide to a small circle of brethren many things that the other apostles did not know, because Jesus had revealed them to him apart, although sometimes to James and John too.

Especially the women followed him more than they did the others, and he took advantage of this, because he realized the women's powers of persuasion and penetration into men's sentiments and ideas. Exhorting wives to obey their husbands, he will later tell them that wives in like manner were to be subject to their husbands so that, even though these husbands might disobey the word, they would, without any word, be won by the behavior of their wives, by virtue of watching their chaste and reverent manner of living. Often a woman, sister

82

or wife, followed him in his journeying. He felt the spirit of the healer, inspired by Jesus, growing in him and, after the first cure of a cripple, the sick, the crippled, and the dying sought him out as a savior.

People came from the surrounding countryside to ask him to tell of Jesus' life and to show him incurables, and he traveled willingly from village to village, where peasants, artisans, and fishermen, poor and humble people all, were more receptive to his words than the shrewd and prosperous city merchants. Thus his fame spread. It was said that at Lydda he had healed a paralytic; in this flowering plain of Sharon the people cried "Miracle" when they saw, walking on the streets, this man who had not left his bed in eight years. Then Peter left Lydda, following the road to the sea.

At Joppa (today's Jaffa) there was already a colony of Nazarenes. Joppa had been an ancient Phoenician city and was still the chief port of Palestine, though the fast-growing Roman port of Caesarea offered competition. Peter went there to seek a favorite disciple who was called Tabitha in Aramaic, and in Greek Dorcas, which means gazelle. Active and beneficient, she wove and sewed tunics and capes to dress the unclothed.

Now weeping women came to meet the apostle, to bring the sad news that Tabitha was gravely ill, on the verge of death, perhaps dead by now. Peter arrived and brought his beloved pupil back to life, to the city's great joy and marvel. In many of his followers, however, the marvel was mixed with worry and suspicion because during the days, or weeks, that he stayed in Joppa, he had no hesitation about accepting the hospitality of a certain Simon, a tanner, which meant that he was staying in the house of a man who exercised an impure trade by handling the carcasses of animals, a sign that he was no longer influenced by Jewish beliefs. But he was to bring about still greater scandal shortly afterward at Caesarea.

Before leaving Joppa, he had a vision. He had gone up to the rooftop to pray, as was the Jewish custom. Although he had certainly not forgotten the Master's precept to pray in the privacy of one's room and one's own soul, with instinctive diplomacy based on good judgment, he probably did not want to offend the Jews.

It was noon and the weather was hot. After the prayer, Peter drowsed lightly and fell into a trance. Earlier, being hungry, he had asked Simon to bring him something to eat, but the trance-like sleep overtook him first. He suddenly saw the sky open, and a tablecloth, suspended by the corners and heaped with every sort of furred and feathered game, was lowered over the terrace while a voice invited him, "Arise, Peter, kill and eat." Since these were foods forbidden by the Jewish laws, Peter drew back. "By no means, Lord, for I have never eaten anything defiled and unclean." But the voice from Heaven said, "What God hath cleansed, God hath purified, hold it not in defilement." At this, the tablecloth full of food was drawn back again to the sky.

Visions are omens, calls and announcements sent by God to men: they are symbolic revelations of unknown or misunderstood truths. What remote truth was wrapped in the veil of that vision in the house of Simon the tanner?

Forty miles away another man had a vision at the same time. At Caesarea, a centurion of the Italian cohort, named Cornelius, a benefactor of the poor, was praying at that moment. He was not a Jew, not even a completely converted and circumcized proselyte, so it was not a Jewish prayer. He and his family were foreigners who had become proselytes of the gate, "the fearful of God," because they liked to be with the Jewish people and loved their monotheistic religion, their customs, their way of treating life as a perpetual waiting for awesome events, and they had learned to pray in their own fashion.

In the centurion's vision, an angel from heaven appeared and told him to send someone to the house of Simon the tanner in Joppa, to seek out a certain Simon, called Peter, who would tell Cornelius what he must do. The centurion was astonished and upset; he did not understand why the God of the Jews should use him, a Gentile, as a messenger. He called two servants and a soldier, who, like himself, were proselytes of the gate, and sent them to Joppa. They sought out Peter; they found him just coming out of his vision and equally worried and confused. Peter listened to the messengers; he then asked the tanner of skins to put them up for the night, and the next day the four set out together.

Two days were needed to get to Caesarea from Joppa by way of the dunes. Thinking over the centurion's invitation and his own vision, putting the one with the other, he understood the meaning of what he had seen in the vision. The Lord admonished him not to consider Gentiles as strangers, and advised him to bring them into the faith of Christ too. This was the truth hidden under the veil of exhortation which had been repeated three times, telling him not to call unclean that which God had purified. And he arrived at Caesarea with a light and happy heart, ready for action. The parable of the return of the prodigal son flashed through his mind like a ray of summer sun.

Cornelius, his family, and the soldiers received Peter graciously. He told Peter about the vision of the angel sent by Heaven. Peter told Cornelius of the life of Christ on earth, and of His death and Resurrection. Then, to the great astonishment of the faithful who were with him, he baptized the centurion.

"Can anyone withhold the water that these should not be baptized, who have received the Holy Spirit even as ourselves?"

But the astonishment of the followers became anger and accusation when Peter returned to Jerusalem. The Galilean fisherman was a man of impulse and instinct, who little tolerated being bridled by the rules of the Law. Let them consider him a transgressor: he certainly did not regret his infringement. But the custodians reproached him. He had been chosen; all the more was discipline expected of him and compromise denied. James was the head of the church, and James must be obeyed. The zealots showed that they were disturbed by Peter's escapades when they appealed to James. The uncircumcized could not be admitted to the community; only to them had the divine gift of baptism been offered.

Peter angrily justified himself before the assemblage. There was agreement and disagreement. At last, humbled if not convinced by his speech, the troublemakers seemed to quiet down. But a breach had been opened in the dike which defended the closed field and, on the day the river overflows, water will go through that breach.

Then, according to golden-winged legend, the centurion Cornelius was flown from Palestine back to the city from whence he had come—Rome. He was the first to bring back to Rome the words heard in Jesus' country. He let fall the pollen gathered at Israel's young plant in the soil of the world's capital at that time.

In those days, Saul returned to Jerusalem.

10

Saul Returns to Jerusalem

When Saul came out of the Arabian desert, his first thought was of Jerusalem, the city where he had studied, where he had grown to knowledge and pride, where he had sinned.

Jerusalem, Jerusalem! The holy name rose to the exile's lips like the beginning of a hymn or prayer. He who left the city for business or adventure kept it always foremost in his thoughts, and secretly hastened the day of his return and wept over his misfortune while away. Never did sons love their mothers the way Jerusalem was loved, not only by those who had been born there, but also by those who had only grown up there, who felt that they had been born a second time in her.

It was a beautiful city. Seven measures of beauty, said the poetry of her people, had descended over the earth: Jerusalem had six of them and all the rest of the world had only one.

Not only that her temples and houses were built of great slabs of stone, not only that the twenty-four market squares were paved with flint; but also great trees grew in Jerusalem as in a garden of paradise and, along with the trees, miracles sprouted.

Foul misery nestled in her alleys and slums, and gross greed invaded porches and synagogues; but there was a generous and prosperous middle ground between the two extremes, which still maintained the courteous custom of hanging a napkin from the door at dinnertime so that anyone who saw it might enter and be seated as a guest at the table. The odor of incense wrapped its walls like a mystic veil and spread as the wind bore it over the hillside cottages, where young women came out to breathe the air, thereby saving their perfumes.

Jerusalem! Jerusalem! It was not an earthly city, but the anteroom to the Celestial Kingdom. Ennobled by myth, its history said that no man was ever wounded in Jerusalem. No one stumbled and fell; accidents never happened to anyone. Fire never raged there. No woman ever had a miscarriage. Never was an oven lacking a Paschal lamb to roast. No one lacked a bed. Never did it happen that a man could not find shelter for the night because the city was too crowded. No house was ever contaminated by pestilence. The city of Jerusalem had never been cursed by God for apostasy. It was beauty; it was joy; it was love. Its countenance shone with a vivid light like a dart of lightning.

Saul was attracted to Jerusalem more by turbulent memories than by serene ones. He had to return to the scene of the crime, among the stones he had bloodied with youthful blood—blood blessed of God—to feel his heart profoundly lacerated by shame and remorse. There was not penitence sufficient to wash him of his past misdeeds. Only God had the power to grant him the pardon he could not give himself or ask of his victims, and he had to gain that pardon with the gift of his whole life.

88

He also had to return to Jerusalem to humble his stubborn native pride and to put the strength and grace of his humility to the test. The teacher of that pride had declared that, more than any fire, it was necessary to stamp out the overheating of the spirit. Now he would kneel at the feet of the saints he had persecuted and injured. He would ask them for light, counsel, and guidance. They had been there first: he was only the last, "the abortion."

They had known Jesus while He was on earth, praying and working; he had met Him after death. Oh, how fortunate they were! He had not had such good fortune. And, if he had had the chance, idiot that he was, he would have refused it. In the Arabian desert he had prayed and meditated at length; he had penetrated into the depths of the mystery of the Messiah, but his spirit was still like a plowed field which lacks a stream of water from a spring. With all his soul he had asked that Jesus appear to him again, speak with him again; and perhaps Jesus had done so, not only to correct and refresh him, but to repeat to him too some of the great words the first disciples had already heard. He had illuminated for Saul that which he had previously learned only from books, in the way that the sun's rays illuminate the forest. He had revealed the ancient prophecies to him, and He had purified Saul's great emotional tumult with the fire of love. He had charted out the message that Saul must etch upon the world. Perhaps there had been long, ecstatic discussions with Paul.

Merchants on their way to the Orient passed him on the caravan routes, and each one brought an echo of the ineffable events that had occurred years before in Galilee and in Judea. Perhaps Andrew, Philip, or Bartholomew passed Saul's retreat in the desert. Saul asked questions and learned from them, and he was already drawing in his mind the great construction to which he must put his hand. But the pillars lived in Jerusalem, and without them nothing solid could be constructed. He must go to Jerusalem.

He decided to stop first in Damascus, to stay there for a little while as a kind of short apprenticeship, to prepare his spirit for direct contact with the apostles. Again he was a guest in Judas' house, and received a fatherly welcome from his good spiritual doctor Ananais and from the other members of the community, which had grown during these three years. They did not make him feel the guilt of his old errors. But they surely assailed him and, so as not to feel them himself, Saul passionately devoted himself to preaching.

From the beginning, his independent spirit, his too personal way of looking at his self-assigned task, could not but arouse much suspicion and some opposition. Could one really believe him? Was he truly convinced? Sincere? Was there not the risk that the old arrogance would rear itself in this contrite and exalted penitent? Was he not one of the usual crackpots, a more intelligent and cultivated Simon Magus?

It was natural that the major enmity should come from his former allies, and it came soon. He was the turncoat, the traitor —he who had been Israel's voice and sharp sword. An order for his arrest was issued by the ethnarch, governor of the city in the name of King Aretas, whose great kingdom of Syria and Arabia had been returned to him by Caligula. He sent a troop of Bedouins, commanded by a sheik, to surround the house where Saul was hidden, and placed sentinels at the city gates. The renegade's fate awaited him, suffering which would have made him worthy of the apostolate, but he had to live if he were to accomplish his mission. The brethren saved his life in the dead of night, lowering him in a basket from a window which opened on the bastions. He was not a heavy man, and the long fast in the desert had made him lighter still.

The great neophyte appeared at Jerusalem, obedient, but
with head held high. To a vehement nature like Saul's, submission assumes aspects of challenge; one of such nature is
proud of his very humiliation. Humbling himself to the saints
of the new faith, he looked his former comrades straight in the
eye. He did not go to live at his sister's house because he had
been disinherited by his father. He sought out Peter instead.
Perhaps Peter came to meet him and opened Mary's friendly
house to him. The only apostles in Jerusalem at that moment
were Peter and James the Less, but there were the deacons
of all the disciples of Jerusalem. They realized that they might
as well place a guarded trust in the new arrival.

To put their doubts to rest, Saul, who was not a man to
lose time by hesitating, immediately went to the Hellenite
synagogues and asked to speak. The blinding flash of revelation and the years spent in the desert had been like a mortal
illness and a long convalescence, and they gave him a more
enthusiastic youthfulness. His language had its earlier impetus
and vigor again, but with a new luminous ardor. Scribes and
Pharisees recognized the young spellbinder, but now his flaming eloquence was directed entirely against them, and they
felt all the anger and scorn of the betrayed toward the betrayer.
The Nazarenes found all the old haughtiness of their implacable enemy in the convert to the faith of Jesus, and it made
them uneasy with a fear of new and irreparable surprises.

In those years a unique life of renewal was going on in
Jerusalem, unbeknownst to any of those inside it. The moral
and spiritual climate of the world was changing, but men's
senses were unable to detect the changes. Later, they recognized
the effects; just as the flowering of the fields, the disappearance
of the snow, and the nesting of birds make spring apparent by
May, even though Nature begins the renewal in March. But it

was not to be long before the world was to be shaken by the great March wind: the beginning of Paul's preaching.

He stayed only fifteen days in Jerusalem.

Until now the apostle's words had been, and were to continue to be, those of explanation and persuasion. They told the new generation about the deeds of Jesus; they repeated those wonderful, gentle words they had heard from Him and explained their meaning, urging conversion on Judea's people. Now Paul, the great convert, raised his voice to shout to the Gentiles about the error in their lives and to admonish them to reform; his words thundered in a tempest. To the older people, it was like hearing the voice of Jesus again, not that of those gentle discourses along the flowering banks of Gennesaret Lake, but that of the tirades in the house of Simon the Pharisee.

One day Saul met Barnabas, who had been his classmate at Gamaliel's school. Barnabas had been converted to the new faith before Saul, without lightning bolts, but with a spontaneous spiritual impulse. He had already acquired great prestige in the community because of his lofty mind and gentle nature.

On the day of Barnabas' conversion, there had been a break between these two old friends, and they had not seen each other since. As a cousin of Mark, Barnabas had been able to get close to Peter. He immediately realized what a wonderful acquisition the new faith had been to this schoolmate of his, this Saul, whose intelligence surpassed them all. Now that the greater number of the twelve were scattered and little news was heard of them, the new-born church lacked a great missionary, a man of valor and adventure. Barnabas brought Saul, Peter, and James together in secret meetings. One thinks that on that first day a certain unease was probably interposed between James, the old leader revered by all, and the young convert, who formerly had been feared by all, the errant rascal who had once dared to raise his hands to James. But any discomfort was conquered by the former's indulgence and the latter's sincere repentance.

In those meetings it was decided that the new convert would carry the word of Jesus beyond Palestine.

It seemed a good idea to get him away from Jerusalem, to take him out of that atmosphere of reserve and suspicion which only time could dissolve, and thus avoid the inevitable friction between the audacious new arrival and those who had been there long before him. For the last arrived can not escape the role of intruder, even if he is better endowed than the others; in fact, his very superiority confers this role upon him. Even if he is willing to humble himself, as Saul tried to do in word and deed, he doesn't succeed, and the attempt to humiliate or belittle himself seemed a particularly offensive and hypocritical way of showing off.

There was also the danger of ambush and reprisal by the betrayed Pharisees. Already zealous cutthroats were roaming around the renegade's hiding place at night. Consequently, a change of air was advised. An armed escort accompanied him to Caesarea by night. There he was put aboard a vessel sailing for Tarsus. They were sending him back to his native land.

His home, the home of his fathers, of his childhood companions whom he had not seen for twelve years! The place where his dream of glory first saw life, that dream which had grown so much in Jerusalem! He had been disinherited by his rich father, who, like any rich man who sees weeds growing in his own backyard, and who lacks the loving wisdom of the prodigal son's father, asked nothing of him. Saul had learned the weaver's trade before learning the Law, and he sought work here as he had in the Arabian desert. This scion of a prosperous family began to live from one meal to the next.

At this time he also entered the synagogues and asked to speak.

Tarsus was a beautiful city, beautiful and spacious, though it would not seem so today from the little recollections left of it. A mingling of Greek and Asiatic peoples with a social and cultural life both Greek and Jewish, it was also a mixture of fetid maritime trade and artistic decorum. At that time it held a few hundred thousand inhabitants. It was extremely corrupt, as were Oriental cities in the empire. It is difficult to give the prize for moral decadence to any one of them—to Alexandria or Damascus, Antioch or Tarsus, Corinth or Ephesus—when Rome outdid them all. Tarsus was a city rich because of its port, busy with merchants from Rome, Egypt, and Spain; and it was also culturally advanced. Its university was famous among the many universities of Asia. Neither Athens nor Alexandria had as many schools of rhetoric as flourished at that time in Tarsus. It was such a hothouse of teachers that the imperial houses of Rome came to Tarsus several times to borrow teachers for their sons.

It was also renowned because of the many illustrious men who had either visited or been sent there to stay. Cicero had been governor of the province at one time, but that office had only served to intensify his typically aristocratic dislike of Jews, who, in his opinion, were greedy, ambitious, and untrustworthy. Caesar had stopped there briefly, just long enough to give birth to the base and baseless rumor of the Gaul conquered by Nicodemus. In Tarsus, spread out on both sides of the Cydnus, with its lazy waters flowing through it between borders of fragrant oleanders, Anthony and Cleopatra met, and the two lovers went back up that river in the Queen of Egypt's luxurious, flower-bedecked galley, escorted by swans.

Augustus did not come to the city, but he always protected

it, and after the battle of Actium, he confirmed its ancient privileges. In the perpetual struggle between Jews and Gentiles that divided all the cities, Tarsus even as Alexandria, Augustus always took the Jews' part, and was generous with decrees to protect their laws, customs, and rites. This shrewd man of politics understood the fable of the lion and the ant better than writers and historians; like the powerful king of the forest, he respected the patient, worried labor of the Jews, as the lion did that of the ant.

Saul asked to speak in the synagogues and began his mission on that day in this place, after the trial flight at Damascus. In a few months, he had infinitely enlarged the horizons of his original concept. After the meditation, the practice of speaking defined the missionary task for him.

What he had learned from the apostles about Jesus' earthly life was not much, but it was enough; and what he had not learned, he was able to divine for himself. He did not need to know any more. The meditation in the desert had taught him more than could be learned in a whole lifetime in the study of the Law. He knew far more than the other disciples. After all, he too had seen Jesus, and Jesus had spoken to him, not only in the lightning flash at Damascus, but also in the quiet peace of his soul. He had not seen Jesus as He was in His earthly life, but as He was when resurrected: only God, no longer man. The limitless silence of the desert had spoken to him with the voice of God. Now he knew everything he was to say to men; from foundation to summit he held the whole edifice, which he had been called upon to build, in his mind; he saw the road he must travel all the way to its end. He is to say later that in those years he achieved the perfection of man "in the measure of the stature of the fullness of Christ." The great convert was already the great initiator.

And from the synagogues of the Jews he went to speak to the Gentiles. He had already made his first speeches and gathered his first converts in the city's suburbs when his friend Barnabas came to visit him, and invited Saul to accompany him to Antioch.

11

Christianity Is Born

After Rome and Alexandria, Antioch was the chief city of the known world. Its population numbered half a million citizens and extended over a vast area between the Orontes River and Mount Silpius. A street eight miles long ran from one end of the city to the other. This street, paved with marble and flanked by statues, was the gift of Herod the Great. A colossal statue of Charon looked down on the city from the mountain top. Antioch's founder, Seleucus, had had the grandiose whim of having it carved out of stone.

The imperial legate of Syria resided in Antioch in a magnificent castle situated on a little island in the river in the city's northern part. The extraordinary installations for illuminating it by night were renowned, as were the cascades, pools, and fountains, which were diverted from the waters of the Spring of Daphne for its adornment. Libanio says that day and night in her streets were the same because of that firmament of burning lights: the only variation was in whether it was God's or man's hand that lit the lamps. With her aquatic riches and

97

sumptuousness, Antioch was a spot of delights and excesses, made even more attractive by the amenity of her setting. Lovely hills, verdant with laurels and cypress, flowering orange, oleander, and pomegranate trees, made a crown around her and rose in undulating knolls in the city's very center. Grapes were cultivated extensively in the valley of the Orontes: they produced heady and fragrant wines. Within the city walls, man's art had added to the beauty and opulence of nature, creating grottoes, gardens, groves, and temples, which invited idleness and delectation. Antioch was also a city rich in trade and traffic, emporium of all the products of the Orient, poured out there by the silk route which began in China, crossed Turkestan, and finished in Antioch.

The friction between the small, privileged class of businessmen, monopolists, and huge landowners, with multitudes of slaves brutalized into forced labor, giving rise to superstitions, fakery, and fanatacism. The luxury and delectations of the former numbed the population's moral sense and emphasized social contrasts. Perhaps in no other city was there such a dense and confused mixture of races, tongues, cults, and vanities as there was in Antioch. Currents of Hellenic thought flowed through the higher circles, while sediments of charlatanism and Asiatic sorcery fermented in the lower depths.

A theater of mimes and histrionics; an arena of processions, dances, sports, and bacchanals; a chamber of orgies and perversions: Adonis and Astarte were its adored deities, along with Daphne, and prurience was fed by pandering, and carnality reigned supreme. It was said to be the metropolis of all lies, the sink of all infamies, although the same could be said with equal truth of every other city. Juvenal wrote that the waters of the Orontes had come to mingle with those of the Tiber, depositing all their mud there, but the muddy Tiber had no need to ask the oriental river's help. However, if a prize is to be given in the precipitate descent to moral decadence, Antioch might easily merit it.

In the midst of these stones and weeds of vice, the seed of the Good News took root and thrived. Where there is much depravity, there is much sorrow; and where the sorrow is great, hope and charity lie. Where the rich are very rich and the poor are very poor, the immense space left empty in the middle is filled with faith in God—or with bloody revolution.

There were many dispersed Jews in Antioch. Increasing rapidly, they soon filled an entire quarter, the poorest naturally. It was called Epirus and was located at the extreme south of the city, far from the magnificence and charm of river and palace. In no other city had their monotheistic religion so successfully drawn converts. The transition from Judaism to the Nazarenes' faith became a natural consequence, and in that melting pot of native Jews, Jewish proselytes, and the "fearful of God," which was the Antioch synagogue, the anonymous Nazarene disciples instituted the Word of Jesus.

The new believers arrived from Cyprus and Cyrene especially, where little Nazarene nuclei had already been formed, and in Antioch their propaganda found receptive soil. As elsewhere, the pagan who had already been converted to Judaism felt a warmth and gentleness in the kindly preaching of the Nazarenes, which was not permitted by the Pharisees' narrow customs. The Antioch community quickly became populous and powerful; it had already given the Hellenite deacon Nicholas to the church at Jerusalem.

It was natural that dissension should break out among so many. In contrast to Jerusalem, here at Antioch Jews and pagans met together for the first time, in prayers, in rites, and in daily living. But suspicion persisted. Serious episodes of friction and scandal must already have occurred, if the apostles sent

Barnabas to conduct an inquiry into the situation at Antioch.

Barnabas was the most farsighted of the new disciples, the just and wise man who had become leader of the liberal party which opposed the narrow and legalistic conservatism of James. Thoroughly versed in the sacred writings and eloquent too, Barnabas was the best suited to bring about the agreement necessary for spreading the Word. Accompanying him were a delegation of notables, well-acquainted with the region's needs and customs.

Barnabas found considerably more than he might have hoped for in Antioch. The little nests of Nazarenes which were taking shape in the city's needy quarter were a happy surprise to him. Within a few years a school of pupils full of good will had grown up, without great teachers, three hundred miles from the source. The great gardeners were lacking, and yet the nursery in the little field was bursting with plants, and the inevitable rivalries of the autonomous forces in formation were owing to this luxuriance. But Barnabas found a sincerity and freedom of feeling in the converted pagans, and in those desiring conversion, which seemed the more amazing in that the life of the Nazarenes was so new to them.

He succeeded in persuading those little nests to gather together into a united force. Then he saw clearly in the city which was open to the western winds what he had already noticed while bound within Jerusalem's walls. From the top of Mount Silpius one could see far wider than from Mount Zion. There was a vast sea over there, and on the other side of the sea, other lands, other peoples, other souls groping in the fog and waiting for a light. He decided he must stay in Antioch because there was much work to do, and he sent news to this effect to Jerusalem.

Then he remembered his old schoolmate Saul, the recent neophyte who had a pioneer's soul and spirit. He knew that he too was working, but in obscurity in Tarsus, where he had been sent partly to test him and partly to get rid of him. Barnabas thought it would be a good idea to open a larger field of action to that lively strength by using it on his mission to the Gentiles, and he went to find Saul in Tarsus and bring him back to Antioch.

Great foresight this, for Barnabas to have understood Saul's genius of mind and spirit before anyone else, and then to draw him out of shadow without fear or envy.

That was 41 A.D., the two friends' fortunate year. Saul was thirty-two or thirty-three years old; Barnabas a few years older. And it was also the auspicious year of the dawning religion.

They felt that their idea of bearing their preaching into the world of Gentiles was an inspiration from on High. God suggested their words and guided their acts. Jesus had not died on the Cross and risen from His grave to redeem only a few people who spoke His language and obeyed the same laws—a mediocre end to such an immense and extraordinary beginning. A good prophet and doctor of the Law would have sufficed for that. The Good News had been announced to men of all kinds; above all to the poor, to the suffering, to the persecuted, to the disinherited and conquered—and the poor, the suffering, the persecuted, the disinherited, and the conquered lived all over the world, in every nation with every tongue. Charity must be like the air, which fills all the spaces not occupied by bodies. The Kingdom of Heaven is boundless in welcoming the worthy, even if the road which leads there is strait.

They preached together in the city of luxury and gaudiness, with its half million inhabitants. They spoke in the synagogues, but people also gathered under the columns and around the pagan temples and listened to them. Jews and Greeks sat together like brothers at the same table, at least as long as Barnabas and Saul remained in the city; and for the first time such incompatible people were seen to form a single family. Also for the first time, the new religion, which had spoken Aramaic up to now, spoke Greek. And the language spoken on every shore of the Mediterranean aided the diffusion of ideas.

The Antioch church rapidly became large, active, and fertile, while that of Jerusalem was crystallizing into the guardian and was no longer the moving force of the faith. The church at Antioch had been born as a congregation of the poor and rejected, but it was quickly enriched with money and prestige because of the entry of powerful and moneyed people, encouraged by Saul and Barnabas for practical reasons. Among the Jews, one Symeon Niger, Lucius of Cyrene, and Herod Antipas' foster brother Manaen stand out. For some time it would seem that the most important post was held by a pagan, Evode.

The communal treasury was quickly filled: Barnabas and Saul decided to reserve part of that money for Jerusalem, which always lived in bitter poverty. Hunger and famine afflicted the Orient, Jerusalem in particular, as during the Bible's cruellest calamities. A prophet of disasters, Agabus, went around heralding years of black misery, and already his prognostications were coming true. Antioch continued to divert herself in opulence, the money in the Nazarenes' treasury did not dwindle, and for a long time the Church of Antioch was the bank which provided funds for the work.

Then the new name was born at Antioch. The Nazarenes, who had called themselves the brethren until then, now called themselves, or were called, Christians. Perhaps the name was first heard from a pagan's mouth, not a Jewish one. Perhaps there was an offensive intent in the name's invention. Perhaps their enemies spread the name more willingly than their friends. But the name spread and stayed. The ephemeral ridicule, if such had been, fell away and the holiness remained. This name was also given to the new era.

Before long the Church at Antioch was the largest one, and it became the radiation point for the Christian religion. Pleased with what they had accomplished, Barnabas and Saul could leave it in good hands and go elsewhere. They took ship at Seleucia and sailed toward Barnabas' home in Cyprus.

This was the right moment to bring the word to the Gentiles, while the Jewish faith was protected by the legate Petronius and the number of Greek converts to Judaism was growing.

12

Peter and the Angel

They had gone to Jerusalem first to bring the offering of money gathered from the faithful in Antioch, and they had found the Holy City overcome by that sense of fear and desertion which is evident where persecution's winds blow, and which makes men prickly and suspicious. The famine was an ill for the poor, but among the bourgeoisie the emperor's favors had brought blissful ease again to the officials and markets. And Ventidius Cumanus had given the death penalty to a soldier who had torn up a copy of the Pentateuch. The favorites again became persecutors of the rejected.

Before he went mad, Caligula had restored to their former rulers the Oriental peoples and the lands which Tiberius had stripped from them. Herod Antipas' nephew, Herod Agrippa, who had been only a tetrarch dependent on Rome, now became king again, as his grandfather had been, and Batanea, Traconitide, Auranitide, Abilene, Galilee and Perea were joined in one kingdom. An astute and corrupt counselor of abominations to the emperor, he had repaid with the skins of others. Later Caligula will go mad and will be assassinated; and Agrippa, master of every intrigue, will obtain Samaria as a reward for having participated in the tragi-comedy which led to the coronation of Claudius.

The pagans could not love the emperor's pawn and pander, who had poured out all favors received from the emperor on the Jewish people, but the Jews held him dear although they had no reason to love him. He was not really Jewish but of Idumean origin, yet he became more Jewish than the Jews. He refocused their religiousness and spurred them to the chase of the new believers; it was he who beheaded James the Great.

Because he had finally become king, he could not admit the existence of other kings and kingdoms in Palestine, an insult this time not to the Roman sovereign but to him; Agrippa. He found intolerable that annoying buzzing in his ears, and in his memory, of a King of the Jews executed and of a Kingdom, even if only in the heavens, which His followers stubbornly awaited. The days of Jesus' trial and torture seemed to have returned, and at this time too the feast of Passover was nigh.

The city was crowded with tents and pilgrims, with prayers and banquets and clamor. Except this time it was no longer the synod but Agrippa the king who wielded political power. Caiaphas had been deposed by Lucius Vitellius five or six years after Jesus' trial: he had been succeeded first by his brother-in-law Gionata, Annas' son, then by Theophilos, another son of Annas, but old Annas still remained the real head. Now King Herod decided to move against Jesus all by himself, and he acted exactly as his uncle had done with John the Baptist. He did not subject James to a trial; he chopped his head off.

He too was to die within a few months at Caesarea, a most revolting death, devoured by worms like a piece of carrion, or so it was said by the men he had persecuted.

Barnabas and Saul may have known about James' death before they entered the city. They sought out the three great pillars of the church, but they found only the wise old man who was protected by his recognized wisdom and, above all, by his natural tendency to conciliate masters and slaves, oppressors and rebels. They turned over to him the money they had collected, then they went to John Mark's house, which was always the meeting place. They hoped to find Peter there, or to find news of him.

John Mark's mother said that Peter had disappeared a few days earlier and she told the pilgrims another marvelous tale. Peter had not been killed as was James; but Herod had ordered his arrest, intending to submit him to the people's judgment. It is difficult to understand and explain this diversity of treatment, though it may have been the consequence of the satisfaction already enjoyed by killing one and of the need to veil that assassination with this open trial. We can also know that the circumstances of, and reasons for, James' capture were different from those of Peter's. Certainly the fiery James—"son of thunder"—was a man to expose himself more than Peter who had become even more watchful now.

Peter was shut up in prison and guarded by four soldiers, who were changed every three hours. It was a cruel prison: in Roman style, they bound the prisoner to the two soldiers in the cell with him while the other two kept watch outside the grate. Scattered through the feasting city, the faithful comrades who were already in mourning for James celebrated Passover without banquets; they prayed instead for their leader's safety.

The church elders were gathered at the usual hospitable house to take counsel as to the best way of attempting, if such were possible, to free the prisoner. They feared that the rabble would shout for his death, as they had with Jesus fourteen years earlier. It was the same kind of mob as before—equally fanatic, wrought-up, and drunken. The priests of the synod were no longer disposed to clemency, and Herod the nephew was more bestial than Herod his uncle.

These, Peter's comrades and students, were more numerous than Jesus' twelve disciples, but certainly no better armed, no bolder, and no more disposed to throw away their lives for that of their leader. These men were endowed with a moral courage which was proof against all, but they were not equally supported by physical courage against authority armed with law and sword. These weak and trusting men did not have the battle training, the razor-sharp shrewdness, which was needed to attack a powerful and evil enemy, warlike and tricky. They trusted in prayer.

Then, in the dead of night, someone knocked at the entrance to the courtyard. The damsel Rhoda went to the door, but she did not open it immediately because, on a terror-filled night like that, one asked first who was there. She seemed to hear Peter's voice calling her by name and she was thunderstruck. Peter had come out of prison! Peter was knocking at the door! She went running through the rooms crying it out. But she did not open the door. The others thought she was out of her mind. It could not be the apostle, they said; you don't escape from prison unless you are freed; you don't break the iron chains that bind you to the jailer. It must be his guardian angel appearing for him.

It might not be a happy apparition. The faithful believed that every living man had next to him the angel assigned to guard him on the paths of earth. If Peter's angel had abandoned his charge, was he then dead? Peter, the father of all! The good counselor, the dauntless guide, the man who more than anyone could talk about Jesus and was loved above all. . . . They went with young Rhoda, who lacked the courage to return to the entrance alone. They opened the door. It was Peter himself, not his angel.

Peter, with his hair awry, his beard untended, his countenance drawn by the trying days, the sleepless nights, the devouring thoughts. And he put heart into them as Jesus had heartened His first disciples when He reappeared after His death. He motioned to them not to speak but to close the door.

Then he told them of his incredible adventure. He could not say whether it was something which had really happened or a vision. Not by men had he been freed, but by God. And if human hands, perhaps without knowing it, without wanting to, had touched his chains, God had certainly guided those hands.

He had fallen asleep late at night in his fetters, and his jailers slept too. A sudden light, like the glare of a lightning flash in a nocturnal storm, had awakened him with a start. He had felt himself jarred by a blow to his side. And a voice, the voice of his angel, urged him: "Up, get up." He had gotten up: his chains were loose, his hands free. "Put on your sandals and fasten them," the voice said. He put them on and fastened them. "Throw on your cape and follow me." He had wrapped himself in his mantle and followed the voice of command and invitation. They had passed among the first guards, who were sleeping. They had passed through the second guards, who also slept. They reached the iron gate, which opened by itself. And behold, here he was, knocking at the entrance of a friendly house. The angel had left him on the street. Human or divine power, he had been freed because God desired his freedom.

This marvelous event was recounted to the two messengers from Antioch by John Mark's mother. She added that Peter had disappeared that same day in the same way he had appeared, almost as a vision; he had not been seen again, nor did anyone know aught else of him.

108

When day came, Herod had sent for the prisoner and, when he was not found, he applied the Roman law and made the soldier-jailers pay the penalty the prisoner should have paid: he killed them. Then he returned to Caesarea, where he had established his kingdom's capital, and was struck and killed by that sudden intestinal ailment the oppressed people called a plague of vermin.

An historian relates that one day he seated himself on his throne to publish the peace treaty between Tyre and Sidon. He was wearing a fabulous tunic, woven and embroidered with silver, which shone and radiated in the sun so as to blind the people prone at his feet. The courtiers acclaimed him god, not man. And the punishment from on high followed.

Barnabas and Saul consigned the money they had collected to James and asked his blessing as a viaticum. Then they set out again for Antioch. When they took leave of their hostess Mary, they asked her to let her son John Mark join them in a prospective voyage to Cyprus. It may have been the young man himself who begged them to take him with them and to persuade his mother to give her permission. The two friends were preparing a glorious adventure—the first Christian mission to a pagan land—and Peter was no longer in Jerusalem to hold John Mark there. The ardent youth felt himself alone, passive and useless, now that his master had disappeared.

Where was Peter? Had he fled Jerusalem, with dogs at his heels, to seek shelter? Or had he too left for adventure, in search of new lands to explore, new souls to conquer for Christ's faith?

None of the outsiders knew anything, but the community must certainly have helped him flee. They knew the elder disciple's spirit, that restless and impatient spirit which had suffered an eclipse on the night of his Master's trial, but in which remorse had later relit the sacred fire. They knew that the Master had entrusted the first-born's heritage to him and that he had forced himself to be worthy by throwing himself headfirst into the lion's cage. Knowing him, they feared for his safety, but they were reassured because he seemed untouchable. He must fulfill his mission: the angel which had saved him from Herod's prison would save him again from the most dangerous straits.

People who returned from business trips to Rome said they had seen him there, or had met other people who had seen him, and it could have been true. He had attracted the censure of rigorous observers when he converted the centurion Cornelius, and the baptized centurion had been forced to leave for Rome. Perhaps in Rome the neophyte's thoughts turned to him and he had called him, as the son calls the father. The centurion thought about him and spoke of him to his intimates and fellow soldiers—of him and of the new religion whose recognized leader was Peter, and of the charity and solidarity and loyalty it preached and practiced. Cornelius spoke too of the extraordinary man they had seen and heard on the banks of the Jordan, whose arcane words they repeated—that extraordinary Man who was not only man but God, the only true God, so different from that species of extravagant deities who were worshipped in Rome's temples and sung in her poetry, though no one really believed in their divinity.

And Peter would have replied to the centurion's loving call; he would have gone to join him, accepting his hospitality, to approve and authenticate with the seal of his own name the work Cornelius had begun.

13

Barnabas and Paul

Since the church at Antioch was established soundly, it could safely be left in the hands of the elder presbyters, who had only to guard against the infiltration of the community by unruly and destroying elements. We have mentioned Symeon Niger, Lucius of Cyrene, and Herod's foster brother Manaen. Ignace, a youthful devotee of Saul who was never his companion, but followed him from afar to gather up his spiritual inheritance later, was then only fifteen years old.

Saul's first missionary voyage in company with Barnabas and John Mark was the shortest in space, but perhaps the longest in time. On your first steps you must heed where you place your feet. You venture, you test and retest; then with knowledge of the road and conscious awareness of your own strength achieved, you speed ahead. Saul saw clearly his goal, but there were many ways to get there. As he journeyed, he widened the horizons around the path he was tracing out. Although his idea had no limits, he realized that one must suit the action to the means at one's disposal. And the prudent Barnabas, who had a practical and sedate mind, was at his side to keep a rein on his impetuousness.

People begin with little essays and experiments to arrive at masterpieces. This applies to poets and men of action. It applies to the river's course as well as to the earth's annual spring awakening. It applies to Jesus, who began with the marriage at Cana, and grew from miracle to miracle to arrive at the Resurrection. Saul and Barnabas were still young, and they had so much time before them.

They sailed toward Cyprus. Since it was Barnabas' homeland, they could be sure of finding safe haven and friends. Saul followed his elder and let himself be guided by him. A sea voyage was easier and less arduous than a journey by land, which must be undertaken on foot through territories poor in roads and rich in dangers. They landed at the port of Salamis, not far from Barnabas' native town of Famagusta.

Even though Aphrodite, the goddess of love and beauty, had been born in the sea of Cyprus, the island was not all beauty and receptivity. The mountainous terrain, with much rock, was partly wild forest and partly planted with grapes. It was sparsely populated by Semitic and Phoenician peoples whose customs were similar to those of our missionaries. It was not rich, and its chief resources were derived from a great and celebrated copper mine, the precious metal which had either given its name to the island or taken its own from it. The cypress too, long-lived and luxuriant here, received its name from the island.

Our missionaries traveled down the south coast, the island's most pleasant and welcoming part, and after sowing their teaching in the small coastal cities they reached the capital on the opposite cape, which was the city of Paphos. The journey of about a hundred miles had lasted from the spring until autumn of the year 45 A.D. During that time, they met another Cyprian initiated to the Christian faith, Mnason.

The Roman consul had his headquarters at Paphos, really new Paphos, and they waited there until the end of the year. It was largely newly-built, reconstructed by Augustus on the ruins of an ancient city destroyed by earthquake a half century earlier. But it could not be called a work of art like the important mainland cities, and historians tell us that the Venus in its temple was a lifeless and deformed piece of stone.

At the end of the year, Saul and Barnabas re-embarked for Asia, and they landed in the nearest roadstead, which was Attalia in Pamphylia. They made a brief stop, long enough to catch malaria, then as the weather improved, they ventured into the mountains. They were left alone at this point, for John Mark did not choose to follow them on this adventure, and he returned to Jerusalem.

Along the Aegean, the burgeoning coastal cities, endowed with art and amenity of climate and prospect as well as a thriving trade, led a sumptous and relaxed social life softened with oriental ease. But the harsh internal territory of Asia Minor's great peninsula was mostly savage desert. Only along the rivers, around the lakes, and in the valleys rolling down to the sea, did a fecund vegetation flourish to produce enchanting prospects. In those verdurous spots little cities had taken root, founded not long before as colonies of Roman veterans and now the oriental bulwarks of the Empire. The rest was sand and rock, amazing spots vowed to banditry. From the desert blew winds of sorcery and superstition.

The two missionaries realized that in all that black magic they had to search out a soil suitable for sowing the Gospel.

Where Greek civilization had transformed the desert into garden, the last roses of art and philosophy dropped, burnt by so much sun. But the new religion must seek out simple uneducated souls, discarding the effects, the knowing, the sophists who would only tangle the skein of their thoughts.

The weather improved and they crossed the Taurus. After a fortnight's difficult travel, passing from the seashore's gentle climate to the mountains' rigor, they reached the capital of Pisidia, another Antioch located more than a thousand yards above sea level. Saul had a fever when he arrived there, and ill cared for, in fact not cared for at all, the fever afflicted him all his life, "a thorn in his flesh." Perhaps it was the recurrent malaria which had poisoned his blood in Pamphylia's swamps.

In the Pisidian Antioch, they found the city of the cult to the moon, meaning to say a clot of the superstition which overspread the entire country. The Celts, who had come down from Northern Europe three centuries earlier in search of sun, and the Orientals, who had come up from the Persian Gulf to open the Mediterranean roads to their markets, had brought their own cults, rites, fetishes, idols and druidic sacrifices mingled with Persian spells among the dissolving leftovers of Greek mythology. Even the god Mithras had his altars there. Simon Magus, proven false in Samaria, may have come to find a more fertile field of action in Syria and Frigia.

They stayed in Antioch all year then; when they were able to leave the new church in the hands of well-trained disciples, they resumed their desert journey. There were hardships and dangers of every sort, from wild beasts to bandits; they suffered hunger and thirst; for long tracts they encountered neither city nor settlement; they slept under the moon. After about eighty miles of traveling they came to Iconium, at that time a colony of Roman veterans which had been granted the honor of calling itself Claudiconium after Claudius, but which was really an ancient city. Like Petra, the city red as a rose, Iconium was as old as the end of time. A stupendous garden of vineyards and orchards, a green island in the middle of prairie and salt lakes.

They stayed about another year in Iconium, bringing the mission also to little settlements scattered among the environs. Certain natural grottoes carved out of the mountains there are still called Saint Paul's Caverns. From Iconium they went eastward, and after crossing Lycaonia, which was the most savage and impenetrable country of all Galatia, they reached Lystra and then went on to Derbe. These were cities situated on a plateau more than a thousand yards high. In this land, Cicero, an exile in a barbarian country rather than the representative of the Roman government, had suffered much fighting against the bandits who bothered him at least as much as the prevaricators and political adversaries of Rome.

The pilgrims stayed another ten or twelve months in Lycaonia, then they decided to return home. Their work had achieved fruition. Converts drew together like families. There were not only young people lit by a fire of enthusiasm which might go out when their teachers left, but mature men convinced of the truth preached to them, who would themselves become preachers of the Good News. Saul and Barnabas left willing disciples in every city they had visited.

They returned well pleased. They had fruitfully spent four years of their youth. Many things had they to say when telling not of the miracles they had accomplished but of the real miracle, the birth of the new religion and the new morality, the disclosing of a conscience of virtue and sacrifice in crude and cultivated minds, and of how the words from their lips had been transformed in the hearts of the listeners in the faith. They also had to ask news of the great churches at Antioch and Jerusalem, for so many events, so many storm winds, pass over men's houses in four years.

From Derbe they could go straight back to Antioch, by way of Tarsus, for the Taurus mountains are much steeper in that region and offer the wayfarer no route save the narrow pass of the Cilician Gates, a fearful and almost impassable spot of hellish gorges. So they retraced their steps in reverse: one doesn't leave the old road for the new.

There were also the little churches left behind on the old road: they wanted to check on their progress, to correct an error where it had showed itself, to give advice to those who asked it and rebuke to those who needed it. Above all, they wanted to dispense the best of encouragements to well-doing—praise. The artist is never content with his work; even after it has been given to the public, he likes to retouch or improve it, and this was especially true of them. Certainly Saul and Barnabas saw ill-made steps on this journey backward over their previous path. Missionaries must have almost supernatural powers of clairvoyance, a spirit open to every current of idea with the certainty of being able to drive them all out so that only their own remain, not mortified but fortified in contrast with the others.

From the experience of four years spent in Asia (this is what the peninsula which is now Asia Minor was then called), the two missionaries came out tempered by the test of fire. They knew they could win, and they brought back sharpened battle arms.

They went back to the sea and made a last short stop at Perga to found another little church, then they set sail for Tarsus, and from Tarsus will land at Antioch.

14

Timothy and Tecla

This is the bare outline of the first journey; it can be colored with some incidents.

In their preaching the two missionaries usually followed this system: they waited for the first Saturday to show themselves at the synagogue, and in the meantime tried to study their ambiance. In the synagogue, after the leader had read from the Law and the Prophets, they asked to speak and announced the arrival on earth of Jesus, the Messiah and Redeemer, resurrected after being crucified by the synod. It is permissible to think that Saul spoke more willingly, especially when interruptions occurred and there were objections to answer. Barnabas upheld and commented on his friend's arguments with personal recollections and evangelical tales learned from Peter and John.

The first effect would be curiosity: a speech on religion always aroused the Jews. Everyone had already read in the Books of the Prophets what was said by the two preachers, but they neither thought nor hoped these prophecies would come true in their lifetime or that they could become participants.

Curiosity crowded the synagogue, and suspicion followed. Cries were raised which became abusive and threatening. From threats to blows was only a short step.

The two missionaries shook the dust from their feet and left the synagogue. It was the ancient gesture which was advised by Jesus should His first apostles find inhospitable reception. "We have fulfilled our obligation to enlighten you," Barnabas and Saul would say. "You don't want us, and we are going to preach to the Gentiles." This had already been their intention—to bring Christ to the Gentiles. They made a good pretext of the Jews' aversion to such an idea to put it into action. One can also think that Barnabas would have preferred to use persuasion, with his conciliating words, since his companion's language sometimes took on a note of imposition. By now, however, he no longer merely accompanied his stronger and more ardent colleague, but followed him.

Passing over among the Gentiles, some of whom were already Jewish proselytes, they did not find completely untouched soil as one might have feared; little fields were already sprouting on the bare steppe and irrigating streams burst from the sand. Little flowers of the Good News budded in the most unlikely climes, arid and unhealthy, for the words of Jesus had fallen partly in fertile soil, partly on the wayside, and partly among the stones, as He had predicted. Were these seeds borne by migratory birds, pollen torn from the trees by winds of marvel and tenderness?

The Messiah had left the earth only fifteen years before; already His existence, at first known only to a few, was penetrating the curiosity and conviction of many. Like the few loaves and fishes of the miracle, the words Jesus had said to His twelve pupils were appeasing the hunger of thousands of the famished ones. Merchants in search of profit, artisans in search of work, persecuted in search of refuge, they carried the

118

echo of the words sowed in Palestine over sea and mountain. The two missionaries had to correct many errors and to explain many obscure events which to the credulous might seem the work of magic rather than divine inspiration, but they often found their task eased: their discourse became more convincing inasmuch as it was a response to the questions of those who wanted to know.

Asia had lost all national sentiment after the Roman conquest, mingling the cult of Augustus with its various religions, and it was particularly suitable for a fruitful mission. The pagan proselytes easily passed over into the religion of Christ which, on the words of the two missionaries, asked neither rites, renunciations, nor mutilations repugnant to their self-respect.

In the midst of hostility, Saul and Barnabas found warm welcome. They quickly formed close friendships, soluble only by death. Suggestions—Barnabas with his intimate and indulgent fellowship, Saul with his fiery words—operated even before they began preaching.

And the purity of their lives was a persuasive example. The two went alone, though John Mark was with them in the beginning. They carried little more than the Master had charged his first disciples to take: a sack, a pair of shoes, a staff. They earned their bread by working. A resting place was offered to them. No woman was with them. The woman, so much a part of the life of Jesus, both man and God, now must keep herself apart from the life of the disciples, who were men only.

The missionaries' strictness imposed morality on the little groups of new churches which gathered around them. In that life in common, an atmosphere of chastity and charity took shape which was more sweetly persuasive than teaching and correction. In this climate the virtue they preached became a habit, almost a need, and their pupils' belief in the divinity was purified of all pagan dross.

At Cyprus, the good work had been limited to a few small cities and had not given forth showy fruits. But it ended with an illustrious acquisition, the Roman pro-consul Lucius Sergius Paulus who lived at Paphos.

The Jewish prophet Bar-Jesus worked his spells here. He was known as Elymas, the sorcerer and wise man, probably a student of Simon Magus. From the public square he had succeeded in insinuating himself into the governor's palace. Lucius Sergius Paulus heard about the two preachers of a new faith and, curious to hear them, invited them to an audience despite the wizard's efforts to dissuade him.

There was a debate which had to end with victory for the Nazarenes. Bar-Jesus had recourse to all the magic arts in his repertory to confound his adversaries and recapture the proconsul who was escaping his power. But the adversaries had the more potent arts and arms of the eloquent Word, and when finally it seemed that the Word was not enough, Saul rose and invoked the Lord's hand against the wretch.

As has been said, Saul did not have a great or imposing physical stature or even a resonant voice; he was transfigured in his disdain and invective by the flame that burnt within him and the spirit that inspired him. They made him into a giant—a superhuman being. The Lord's hand really did descend on the sorcerer, who lost sight and sound and went groping like a blind man in the dark.

Nothing else was needed. Already inclined toward the human and celestial peace of soul heralded by the new faith, the proconsul declared himself converted. He was a well-culivated man, versed in the natural sciences and the arts, and he loved to surround himself with a following of young philosophers and writers: his conversion therefore made an impression and brought followers.

After the centurion of Caesarea, this was the first Roman citizen known to history to have been converted to the Christian religion. They could leave the island satisfied with the work accomplished and sure of greater conquest.

And Saul is already Paul. It was natural that the first victory had given him that self-assurance and security which fortified the apostles. From this place and time he takes his second Roman name and eliminates his first Hebrew name, in homage to the proconsul's conversion and as souvenir of his first spiritual son. Haughty affirmation that from now on his life will be wholly dedicated to the pagans and no longer to the Jews? It is not important. What is certain is that now, as he leaves the island and returns to the mainland, he is no longer Barnabas' companion but the leader. The historian Luke, who has placed the name of Saul after that of Barnabas until this part of the tale, the young man after the older, now puts it first, and he too calls him Paul.

But he lost his other comrade when he arrived in Asia. Fatigue and reluctance to effront more severe trials? Inability to tolerate Paul's growing authority, which assumes despotic aspects, coupled with displeasure over the diminished authority of his cousin Barnabas, to whom he was especially bound? He may also have been disturbed by Paul's ever more apparent inclination toward the pagans.

It wounded Paul like a blow. When one has grasped the handle of the plow one does not look back: the Master had said it; he would repeat it. He let John Mark go, but he did not forget the offense. For if it were homesickness this was no excuse, missionaries did not suffer from homesickness. "Who doesn't leave mother, father, and brothers to follow Me is not worthy of Me." The Master had said this too, and the missionary obeys.

Paul arrived at Pisidian Antioch with his spirit swelled by success. He knew well that he was not the Messiah—oh, folly of youth—but the herald of the Messiah must act as though he were. He had clothed himself in Christ, and the new habit had become his soul.

Clearly he now sees the road that has been assigned to him: he knows he must travel over it, and he will travel it until the end. He knows where he wants to go. The outline of the mission intended for him is complete in his mind. After the meditation in the Arabian desert and the Antiochian essay, the test of Cyprus had completed his definition of his mission. He takes every liberty in the methods and limits of this mission, asking no one's permission, because it is entirely his own conception. And he is superbly aware of this: "I have set thee to be a light to the Gentiles, that thou shouldst be for salvation even unto the ends of the earth." Was it not Jesus who spoke thus to him? He is certain that he heard the voice.

A little thing, a fleeting thing, would the new religion be if it were only to govern the descendents of Abraham, as the Mosaic Law governs them. And Jesus' crucifixion would have been useless if His death were to redeem only two or three millions of the Jews and to abandon the unknown multitudes to sin, like disinherited children. The new religion is not a banquet of the privileged. He will call both Jews and Gentiles to Christ, and if the Jews chase him out, his decision is justified, even for his adversaries. It will be a joy to affront beatings, stonings, chains. One has to earn the title of Apostle to the Gentiles with suffering too.

He presented himself in the synagogue and gave a long speech which began with the first patriarchs and went down the long stairway of the prophets to Jesus, resurrected to redeem all, and concluded with an injunction to free themselves of the chains of the Mosaic Law, almost as a threat. Naturally, after a few weeks the Jews no longer wanted to listen to him, and he made himself heard to the Gentiles, who listened willingly. Therefore, the Jews became angry. Stirred-up by "women of position" and "leading men" of the city, they got their hands on him, and on Barnabas, and gave them a touch of the stick, and more than once too. They took the Roman role of applying punishment without a trial. Finally, they chased them out with stones.

Legend gives Paul a fairest adventure at Iconium, and at Lystra history comforts him with the acquisition of a loving family.

A solid citizen named Onesiphorus, who had heard of these Jewish wayfarers, bearers of religious news, and who may have been expecting them, came to meet them and begged them to accept his hospitality. Curious family, friends, and neighbors assailed the door. Paul spoke, and Onesiphorus' house in Iconium became the first church in Lycaonia. After the speeches recounting and explaining Jesus' life came the meal, with sharing of bread and prayer. And the converts grew.

One day Paul made a speech in praise of virginity, and the people who couldn't fit into the house listened from outside, through the open windows. A young girl named Tecla, already betrothed and approaching her marriage day, listened from her house across the way. She was so strongly moved that she rejected her betrothed that evening and decided never to marry.

Though personally celibate because of his apostolic principles, Paul was not against the state of matrimony in the church, and would one day explain in a great letter his ideas about marriage, women, love, and separation. At this point, he meant to speak only about the purity woman must guard in her soul and her flesh as an immaculate flower. Perhaps there passed through his mind Jesus' sharp words to the woman of Samaria with her five husbands. But Tecla was inclined to melancholy, and she drank from these words more than their meaning and intention. Arguments arose between the two families because of the broken engagement, and the family fights were followed by a rising of the people. "The girl is bewitched! Saul has turned her from her duty. Give it to him!"

He was thrown into prison. The bewitched Tecla was also a rich heiress, and she gave the gatekeeper of her great house a golden bracelet so that he would open the door for her secretly at night. She gave the jailkeeper a silver mirror. She wanted to see the apostle, to listen to him again, tell him her secret, offer him her soul. Full of lofty wisdom was this nocturnal dialogue of the apostle and the virgin, but it was brusquely interrupted by the hurried arrival of relatives and soldiers. Tecla's flight had been discovered, and they had found the girl. They subjected her to torture and abuse, which she accepted smilingly. Paul was again beaten and stoned. He had to flee from Iconium, and Barnabas followed him.

At Lystra he was received by a half-Greek, half-Jewish family, which welcomed him to their house every time he returned to, or passed through, Lystra. The old grandmother, Lois, was Jewish and the mother Eunice was also Jewish, but she had married a pagan and was now a widow. The son Timothy, a youth of extreme sensitivity, such as is often born of a mixed marriage, was fifteen years old, or a little more. Paul had no difficulty in capturing his soul, for that candid and open soul was entirely ready to be taken by such a vehement master. It was a meeting of destiny because Timothy will grow to light in the shadow of Paul. He will help his master bear the pilgrim's sack and write his letters. He will be at his side in the hours of anguish and of hope until the very end. He will be his son.

The mother and grandmother, who knew the Jewish laws

124

and customs, told Paul, a Jew, that by his father's wish the boy was not circumcised. Paul replied that the omission was of no importance for a Christian. This was the first open declaration of a thought which will be the pillar of his teaching.

Within the warmth of this affectionate family, life at Lystra would have been less agitated if a curious event which overturned everything had not taken place. Since there were few Palestinian Jews at Lystra, without this incident there might have been no scuffles. It happened that Paul cured a cripple, and the people were so overjoyed and full of wonder that they mistook the two missionaries for two gods and ran down the streets crying loudly: "The gods have come down to earth! Come see Zeus and Hermes!"

Zeus, tall and majestic father of the gods, was naturally Barnabas: Paul, thin and sharp-featured, was Hermes. This was also because Paul spoke readily. Already the head priest, whose place was at the city entrance, wanted to perform a sacrifice, together with the crowd, of a pair of oxen that had been chased to the gates.

Paul and Barnabas set themselves against this silly rumor, which had become an unexpected obstacle to their preaching. If those people became stubborn about wanting them as gods, no strength would suffice to dissuade them. So they, too, raised their voices; they cleared space for themselves in the unruly crowd; they tried to rid themselves of this disgusting idolatrous homage, proclaiming their miserable mortality and the immortality of the true God, the Highest, Who created the world and all the peoples in it, past, present, and future. The true God is not to be propitiated with sacrifices.

But these were words on the wind. Finally some Jews from Antioch and Iconium, who had manhandled them in the latter city, arrived and they provoked the people into stoning them here too.

It was a collective assault by almost the whole region. Barnabas, somewhat neglected as a target, was able to get out of it with a few bruises. Paul was left for dead under the stones. He was to bear wounds and broken bones for a long time. His stigmata from Jesus, he will say later.

The brethren saved him, keeping him hidden in the house of Lois and Eunice: when not even that house was safe, they took him to Derbe where they were able to give him better medication for his wounds. There he was given a bed in the house of a certain Gaius, a man who became his friend and host from that time on.

They preached the Gospel at Derbe too and, since that city was inhabited only by pagans, there were calmer days. Then they retraced the road to Sebaste and went back down to the sea to embark for Antioch.

126

15

The Council of Jerusalem

At Antioch, the great Antioch of Syria, the veterans of the long voyage were received like returning conquerors, though without crowns of laurel and blare of war horns: they were conquerors of souls. News of their victories had preceded them, and the many brethren of the community jammed into Singone Street to get a closer view of the worn and weather-beaten faces of the victorious heroes who had left four years earlier in pilgrim habit. Paul and Barnabas were also pleased to find the first church, author of Christianity's name, in full bloom.

But there were events going on in Jerusalem, and they had news of them in Antioch, which put a little sorrow into the rejoicing. There were even suspicious persons about in Antioch, whose apparent helpfulness only masked a curiosity to overhear their conversations and spy on their movements. They were people driven from Jerusalem by the usual zeal, envy, and jealous foment. First they tried covertly to arouse opposition to the words and ideas of Paul, then they openly proclaimed that the two preachers erred, and that it was sacrilege to follow their teachings. The Law of Moses must be rigorously respected. To be truly Christians the Gentiles who wanted to be converted must first be circumcised. If not, they could not gain admission to the church.

Circumcision had become a point of issue at Jerusalem, and Paul's enemies, whose number increased along with his power, focused primarily on this point to destroy that power.

There occurred in Jerusalem contradictions strange in appearance but inevitable and logical in every revolutionary movement. The old leaders of the church, clustered around James and considered themselves all the more the exclusive recipients and guardians of the word as Paul tried to take possession of it and spread it through the world: by a kind of spiritual osmosis they were going back to their original way of thinking. It was natural that they should be affected by their conversion since, even though Christianized in their emotional outlook, in their minds they remained Jews. Living in the traditional climate of the temple, breathing that atmosphere, attending those rites which, once denied, are reborn in the sweet aura of childhood memory, mingling in daily affairs with those Jesus had attacked, they were inadvertently induced to take up some of their former Hebrew practices again. Jesus had been above these practices: they were not able to break away from them. They still held the faith of Jesus to be compatible with obedience to the formulas of the Law. Venturing into the world, Paul and Barnabas heard the world's hopes and aspirations: closed up in Jerusalem, they could not hear those voices.

It may also have been diplomatic to draw near to their Jewish adversaries. Every weapon is permissible for gathering new members; Paul too will say this one day. To be fair to James, that equable distributor of rights and wrongs, conversions among the Pharisees were not lacking. But was there not a Trojan horse hidden in those conversions?

With their own proselytes, the Jews had never been too demanding. They had not always insisted on circumcision. Old Ananias had given an example with Izate, king of Adiabene. There were those who, if it could have been done without stirring up gossip, would have gladly omitted the harrowing rite themselves. They were already beginning to feel the results of this operation, which obliged them to keep themselves apart in the public baths to prevent exposing themselves to the public jests of the Romans. For this reason alone, more women than men converted to Judaism. And because of the misunderstanding about this rite among the Gentiles, there were a greater number of Hebrew women married to pagans than Gentile women married to Jews.

But the Christianized Jews were uncompromising, and the sarcasm, the scoffs, the insults, added to this intransigence. For them, circumcision was the distinctive mark of the chosen people, the mark of their belief, and they were unaware of the implicit contradiction between the observance of any Mosaic rite and the redemption offered by Christ. Therefore, they sent observers to Antioch to note the practices of the new believers.

Paul and Barnabas resisted at first. God wants mercy—not sacrifices. Above all, even apart from principles and convictions, the success of their efforts and the fervor of the neophytes would have convinced them to persevere because they felt the truth was with them.

Paul did not have a pleasant recollection of James. That new Jeremiah must be venerated because he was venerable and honored by all but, with all due respect to their elders, young revolutionaries are not obliged to follow them on their old paths. It did not matter what James had once done: what mattered was what he was doing now. James' prudence was weakness in Paul's eyes, because James did not realize that the lately-arrived zealots were trying to separate the church from Jesus, not completely understanding that the redemption announced by the Gospel was not the privilege of one race, but was rather mercy distributed to all peoples—a moral and religious foundation for the future. Thus the sun was created to illuminate every part of the earth which circles around it, not just one hemisphere.

But he who wanted truly to serve Jesus and truth now needed the virtue of humility more than anything else. He must obey—obey God. And the authority of the church in Jerusalem must be supported, even with the sacrifice of one's own pride. Paul decided to bow to the leaders' authority: he went to Jerusalem. By now Barnabas was his only follower. They made use of the journey across Phoenicia and Samaria to spread the doctrine.

In Jerusalem, he decided to meet first with the leaders, one by one, in their houses. Ardent in public speaking, Paul was more persuasive in conversation and, in that face consumed by fever, with those deep, flashing eyes, his quiet words became even more impressive. He told them of his adventures and misadventures, of the candor and fervor of those young pagan maids and youths who vowed themselves to Jesus, of his plans for the future, and of the ends he wanted to achieve and would achieve if they gave him freedom of action.

This was the vision of Christianity triumphant in the world! The apostles were moved and defeated by Paul's words. He was quite presumptuous, this recent rival; but he put so much soul, so much sincerity, and so much spirit into his passion that they could not deny him one of the top posts. They decided to bestow the title of apostle on him too; he who had never seen Jesus. Paul knew that it means more to deserve a title than to have one, and he was an apostle with or without the title; but titles have their uses: they bring the official seal to the one who bears them. He would be the apostle to the Gentiles, as Peter was over the others as apostle to the Jews.

At the assembly things went differently. According to the historian, there was much argument. There can not be an assembly without much argument; that is, much noise and talk. Especially the young Pharisee zealots became excited, eager to acquire the prestige they were without, while the renegade Paul had attained so much in so few years. They were forewarned: they had heard rumors from other places; perhaps they had been put on their guard by John Mark's sudden return and by what he had told of Paul's sayings and doings in Cyprus —but really they feared that the intruder wanted to found a new religion and make himself its head.

Then Peter rose to speak and calm the storm.

"Brethren, yourselves do know that in the early days God made a choice among you, that through my mouth the Gentiles should hear the word of the Gospel and should believe. And God, who knoweth the heart, bore them witness, giving to them the Holy Spirit even as He had done to us; and He made no distinction between us and them, cleansing their hearts by faith. Now therefore, why do ye provoke God, that ye should lay a yoke upon the neck of the disciples, which neither our fathers nor ourselves have been able to hear? But we believe that we have been saved through the grace of the Lord Jesus, in like manner as they."

Murmurs of comment followed on these equable words of Peter then, when there was silence again, James, the head of the church, rose to speak. He reaffirmed Peter's words, citing the ancient prophets as witness, and himself added the conclusion of ancient wisdom which placed virtue and truth in their midst.

"Therefore my judgement is that we do not harass further

those among the Gentiles who are turning to God; but that we write to them that they abstain from the pollutions of idols, and from impurity, and from what is strangled, and from blood. For Moses from early generations hath them that preach him in every city in the synagogue, being read every Sabbath."

He did not touch on circumcision which was the sore spot of the disagreement; therefore, he eliminated the obligation. But that silence could also have been interpreted differently, almost as a door always open to discussion; because they knew that mutilation, repugnant as it was to most, could always be a barrier against the Gentiles' invasion. And the reference to Moses, ever present in the synagogues, was such as not to discourage the rigid observers of the Law. So the zealots said it was all right to close an eye to the doings of the enlisted men and give them freedom of choice, but the leaders were expected to set an example of respect for the Law, which was the bulwark of the people and alone could give them happiness. Paul, circumcised himself, should begin by circumcising his young friend Titus, whom he had brought with him from Antioch.

Titus was a young Antiochian Gentile who had caught Paul's attention on his return from his journey. He had chosen him as a pupil to be trained for the apostolate. Barnabas was of equal rank to Paul. Since John Mark had left him, he felt the need of a young devotee to replace the deserter.

Titus was uncircumcised: Paul had never subjected him to the operation, though he would not have been against it if the youth had requested it. Now that his adversaries insisted on it, he sharply refused. Only at the end of his stay in Jerusalem, when he had obtained satisfaction on all fronts and had been given the title of Apostle to the Gentiles and a document had been issued by the leaders which outlined the decisions of the council, did Paul deliver his young companion to the ceremonial knife. He did not bow before an imposition: he spontaneously offered a gesture which was of no importance to him. The distinctive mark of the chosen people was only a rite to him. Perhaps Titus himself had requested it to spare his master annoyance.

So Paul could return to his Gospel, victorious at Jerusalem too. Consider the company of the two youths assigned to him, Judas Barsabas and Silvanus or Silas, a respectful tribute by the leaders. They followed him to Antioch, attesting with their presence the perfect accord reached in the Council and the new authority vested in him, Paul. They also bore a letter of credential which said: "The brethren who are apostles and priests, to the brethren in Antioch, Syria, and Cilicia who are from the Gentiles, greeting. Whereas we have heard that some from amongst us have disturbed you with their words, subverting your souls, to whom we had given no charge; it hath seemed good to us, and we have come to one accord therein, to choose brethren and send them unto you with our beloved Barnabas and Paul, men who have pledged their lives for the name of Our Lord Jesus Christ. We have therefore despatched Judas and Silas, who gave themselves and also will tell you these same things by word of mouth. For it seemed good to the Holy Spirit and to ourselves to lay no further burden upon you than these necessary things, that ye abstain from idol-offerings and from blood and from what is strangled, and from impurity; from which preserve yourselves, and it shall be well with you. Fare ye well."

And they added a recommendation to collect money for the poor brethren of Jerusalem. The theological question of Grace and the Law had not been faced. And officially the name of Barnabas was still placed in front of Paul.

Paul continued on the path he had set for himself. Don't pour new wine into old vessels else the vessel will break and the wine will pour out, Jesus had said, and His precept was Paul's entire program. He cannot use the old vessels of the Mosaic Law to hold the new Christian theology. Had he heard those words repeated by the apostles? Or did he know them from his own inspiration?

16

"I Withstood Him to His Face"

But tranquil and peaceful days did not ensue among the divided spirits.

The insistence on the necessity of abstaining from the flesh of animals killed in sacrifice and from fornication, though seemingly honest, contained hidden tricks, because the first prohibition forced the new Christians to leave their usual market to buy meat only at the Jewish butchers, and the second was extended even to cover mixed marriages.

Paul felt himself victorious because he had been granted the dignity of apostle and he had obtained his "Christian liberty." But the concessions of others did not satisfy a soul so full of the conviction of its own rightness. Since he felt that Jesus lived in him, he was obliged to obey only that inner Jesus. Besides, a Pharisee himself, he knew the Pharisees and knew that they had unwillingly consented to recognize his leadership. Meanwhile, both to remove himself from these worries and to confirm his legitimate authority, he was preparing a new journey to farther lands.

His enemies had not ceded but conceded, which could have sufficed to save their self-respect, but it was difficult for them to admit that the last-arrived, the wild revolutionary, should come to overturn their established order, and lord it over the church which had only received him out of kindness, and give lessons to them, who had been educated at the school of Jesus—he who had studied at the school of the Pharisees. Perhaps they were not yet convinced that the former persecutor was sincere in his new sentiments, that the old wolf had shed his skin and vice all at once. He said he had come to Jerusalem to ask the saints for official investiture, but in reality he let them understand that he did not need them: he had already assumed office himself.

They also made their plan—to act as if they were with him in order to keep close watch on his movements. They would not put a wrench in the gears, but they would let him go and later undo what he had done. Since he wanted to travel, they would construct golden bridges for him, but they would cut those bridges behind him. They sought James' support for this strategy and that of James' brothers, Judas and Simon, thinking that since they rather feared Paul they could not like him.

Peter did not fear Paul and he loved him much. The chief pillar of the church at Jerusalem had realized before anyone else the superhuman powers of the convert. The humble fisherman of Bethsaida possessed the seer's gift as no one else did; and for this too he was the heir of Christ. Himself uneducated, he was dazzled by the other's enormous culture. Impulsive and instinctive, he felt the other's superiority, his reflective and inspired spirit. They were two different natures; but with all the inevitable friction and contrasts of these natures, they were destined to come together lovingly and with reciprocal respect.

136

A man who paid little heed to principles and much to feelings, Peter realized that Paul was on the right road: the new faith must be a spiritual religion, not formalistic or enchained by a law which established 248 precepts and 346 prohibitions. He who had already baptized the centurion Cornelius was in a position to see that Paul's open way in the world was the way of truth. Perhaps the young Tarsian's audacity made him a little nervous even while he admired it, and his own natural friendliness was reined by the stiffness of the others. Certainly he would have emulated Paul joyfully. He may already have been in Rome during the previous years and, expelled by Claudius' edict, may have yearned to return. For this reason, he would have followed Paul to Antioch after the council, curious to study his ways, his methods, his actions. He was then about fifty-five years old: Paul ten years younger.

At Antioch the two great knights of the new faith now met head on.

Because of his fortunate nature, Peter was friendly with everybody. He stayed at the houses of both Jew and Gentile, accepting invitations to dine from the one and the other, and eating naturally all that was offered to him by men ignorant of the Law.

But the zealots still claimed that his actions, even his presence alone, vitiated Paul's influence at Antioch—instead he supported and gave weight to that influence. And when Peter's actions were known in Jerusalem they were considered weakness, and energetic measures were requested of James. It was necessary to take care of the caretakers. More effective agents were sent who recalled Peter to greater respect for the Law. Peter obeyed.

He was no longer seen among the Gentiles. He ate only at Jewish houses, in Jewish style. There was no harm done:

he did what he always had done. But Paul considered it an unworthy pretence. Pretence, however, before or after? With the Gentiles or with the Jews? A way of contenting him, Paul —or the zealot messengers and the leaders at Jerusalem? The worst of it was that the others also followed Peter in his compromising—above all Barnabas, the trusty and loyal Barnabas. Paul was exasperated.

In the midst of a public meeting, he attacked Peter: "If thou, for all that thou art a Jew, livest like a Gentile and not like a Jew, by what right dost thou constrain the Gentiles to live like Jews?"

"I withstood him to his face," he will say later in a great letter and will make a boast of it. But perhaps in that moment he was overcome by scorn—an outburst of rage, and when he later wrote the letter of recollection he was embittered by his disillusionment. Above all, he abhorred in men of action weakness of doing and not doing; and Peter's weakness, which was rather humility and true love of peace, seemed to him an unworthy double game.

He was going through one of those moments of pride that burned more hotly in him after submitting to a humiliation. What circumcision! What law! What difference between Gentiles and Jews! If justice lay in the Law why would Jesus have died? But Jesus rose and the Law died. It was dead even before, in view of the fact that it, the Law of Moses, had condemned and killed Jesus. He himself, Paul, was too dead, according to the Law, to live in God. With Christ he has been nailed to the Cross, and Christ lives in him. He is only the sheath of that shining blade.

The man who had thought he was the Messiah in a superb folly of youth, now knows very well he is not: but he is the man who best understands Him, the one designated to understand Him. He is His messenger, above all the others. And if the others saw Jesus with their own eyes for a short time, he lives with Him constantly in his soul. They listened to him: he is inspired by Him. Blessed are they who believe without having seen, the Master had said: he is one of those. Faith makes the invisible visible.

He was right in his ideas even if he was not right in his methods. And in the eyes of those around them, he who is quiet and endures is more likable than he who, being in the right, imposes his rightness with offensive ways. Barnabas too had been hurt by Paul's strong words and touched by Peter's humble silence. This was Paul's greatest sorrow that sad day at Antioch.

He prepared for a new journey, but Barnabas no longer followed him.

Barnabas loved the perils of the arduous roads, but he also appreciated the benefits of harmony within the church. To fight against outside enemies, yes; but not to seek opponents inside: they must live in peace with all the brethren. Paul did not tolerate opposition and criticism, and his spiritual domination became despotic. To get along with him therefore, one felt the need of another companion to relax with.

So Barnabas proposed that Paul take his cousin John Mark back with them again. Paul refused. The plowman who had turned back was no longer worthy to go forward. So Barnabas separated from Paul. The partnership that had breached the threshold was broken. This was the saddest event in the early years of Christianity.

A flaw in the men, not in the ideas: in the stones, but not in the cement that held them. And it was useful in order that the Gospel could be spread by many missions. Paul and Barnabas separated but they were to meet again. Too different to write the same book together, they will meet again and can exchange the pages each has written. Perhaps Barnabas' company, which provided the counsel of reason and the reign of prudence, would have saved the venturesome Paul some bitter disillusionments. And behind Paul's adventures, Barnabas' actions too would have come out into the sun of history, instead of stumbling in the dark of legend. For legend will take the Cyprian missionary all the way to the Po Valley to found the church of Milan.

They separated. Barnabas went back to his native isle of Cyprus with his cousin: Paul breached the borders of the Orient by land and sea: Peter returned to watch over the difficult situation at Jersualem before he too took to the road.

But Paul could not go alone to unknown countries where there was no one to meet him, especially now that his health was declining. He had recurrent attacks of the malaria he had caught in the Pamphylian swamps and not attended to, with the usual intermittency of tertian fevers, re-awakening in his flesh "the thorns" of what may have been a hereditary blight. But he found young people who wanted to follow him.

Of the two emissaries sent to Antioch by Jerusalem to bring Jews and Gentiles the document of the Council and its accord; one, Judas, had already gone back to Palestine; the other, Silvanus, was to be overwhelmed by Paul's influence and unable to part from him. The prospect that Paul offered—hardships, hunger, beatings, prison—far from deterring young men, only drew them all the more.

Titus and Silvanus were the new companions of the Apostle to the Gentiles.

17

Toward the West by Sea

They did not board a ship this time but went by land. Paul was anxious to revisit the church in Galatia, like any good worker who wants to check on the work already completed before setting his hand to another job.

It was a more arduous and adventurous trip than the first. They set off in the late spring of 52 A.D. on the Roman Road across the pass of Beila. The Taurus mountains of Cilicia, which they avoided the first time, are considerably wilder than the Taurus mountains of Pamphylia, and the passage through its gorges by three helpless and ill-supplied pilgrims was an undertaking of persons vowed to death. The path is so hemmed-in between steepest cliffs that the story is that one time the Romans barred it with real doors nailed to rocks, hence the name Cilician gates.

After ten days they reached Derbe. Then they passed through Lystra and Iconium and reached Pisidian Antioch. Up to this point, the road had been long but familiar. At Lystra Paul found Timothy and learned how the youth, surrounded by a family of devoted women, had grown up in his love and in his faith. He asked the mother and grandmother to entrust Timothy to him and took him along too.

From Pisidian Antioch it would have been pleasant to veer westward toward the florid coastal cities of the Aegean, but the missionaries sought poor and uncultivated lands for their mission. They ventured through the plateau of Frigia, a harsh setting of geological ruins, and for several weeks they went into the desert. They slept wherever they found a heap of straw; they ate hard bread and handfuls of olives. Paul was to remember those days particularly when he wrote the letter to the Corinthians covering the course of his whole life, and he wrote:

> . . . in journeying often, in perils from rivers, perils from robbers, perils from mine own nation, perils from the heathen, perils in city, perils in wilderness, perils in the sea, perils from false brethren: in labour and toil, in watchings often, in hunger and thirst, in fastings often, in cold and nakedness. . . .

He was not a man to beg for pity, but he wanted his merits recognized.

They had crossed Asia and reached the mountains of Mysia, and he was still uncertain about the road to take. To the north, toward Bythnia and Pontua, lands still unexplored by evangelists, or to the sea and the countries of ancient civilization. He wrapped himself in prayer, as he was wont to do at the hour of great resolution, and asked inspiration of Heaven. This time Heaven indicated the western road.

By sea, then, by sea to Greece, to Rome, toward the columns of Hercules. After the dreariness of rock and plain, they now crossed beautiful regions, fertile and smiling. Romans had

142

fallen in hordes to find in these gardens and fields the abundance that was drying up in their own much trodden and exhausted peninsula. And when they settled there, the riches of the soil, the amenity of the landscape, and the serenity of the skies produced an ease and joy of living that softened the Latin temper with sweet Asiatic idleness. To remain holy one had to escape as soon as possible.

But Paul never let himself be attracted or distracted by his physical setting, even by the most gentle and welcoming scenes which melted the heart and led the mind to serene reverie. Different in this than was Jesus, he seemed to be insensitive to the blandishments of the pastoral idyll, to the invitation of those irresistible works of art which are the beauties of the plant world. Perhaps the harsh concentration of his every faculty on a single thought filled him completely, excluding any divergence of feeling or serene joy of the senses. His contemplation could only be interior meditation.

They rested at Troas, within sight of the Aegean: Alexandrian Troas really, one of the many Alexandrias scattered by the Macedonian king on his victorious march. At Troas, a fifth comrade joined the little brigade: the doctor Luke, an Antiochian Greek too, who had been presented to Paul at Antioch and had then dropped from his sight. A well-educated man, traveler, and navigator, Luke was at that time practicing his profession at Troas. He left the sick to follow Paul and was devoted to him from that time on, admiring him, but remaining always in the background. And it may have been he who finally convinced the master to put to sea for Greece.

His mind full of Luke's good advice, the apostle had a dream. He dreamed that a Macedonian man came to him and begged him to pass through Macedonia to succor those abandoned folk. It was the voice of the Lord, who spoke in the voice of the man of his dream, and Paul followed the Lord's voice.

They took ship, made a brief stop at the island of Samothrace, and landed at Neapolis in Thrace.

Thrace in those days was one of the most superstitious areas of the earth because of the degenerative pattern which had followed on the rites and spells of the Orphic mysteries. Its population was spoiled by drunkenness and collapsed in vicious sloth. They were not obstacles which could dishearten Paul, but it took too long to demolish them and, as the road expanded, he felt his life draining away. He was in a hurry to be on his way.

By a rocky trail halfway up the Pangeo, the mountain of gold that had enriched the Macedonian dynasty, he reached Philippi, the city of the republic's end and the empire's beginning.

It was like a minuscule Rome, so much did its architectural plan resemble a metropolis. Augustus had founded a military colony there in memory of his victory, and exempted it from tribute. The colony flourished on the advantages bestowed on it by the emperor. Life was orderly, home-loving, courteous. Since there were few Jews, there was no synagogue. Paul stayed there only one season, then he went on to Amphipolis.

He reached Amphipolis in one day on the Roman Via Ignazia. Here the landscape became gentler, and the wayfarers found a familiar vegetation of vineyards and gardens among blue fields of flax. A land of sparkling, sweet waters, one of the most attractive spots was the nearby Apollonia and its lake. But Paul's goal was Thessalonica, the growing city which had been named after Alexander's sister, and he crossed

Apollonia without stopping and reached the capital of Macedonia. Here the little group made a long visit.

Thessalonica was a great port and a great market, enriched by its trade in stuffs and hides, and the products made therefrom. The hot springs on its outskirts were celebrated. When Cicero was confined to a villa there he certainly suffered much in his spirit but not in his physical life, for the city's panorama of hills and sea resembled the Latin landscape. Vineyards and orchards of orange, apple, and other fruit trees crowned the industrious and populous city sloping down to the amphitheatre of the sea. There was a synagogue richly endowed by the munificence of bankers and merchants. Paul preached there for five or six months; then he was forced to flee from Thessalonica too.

He sought shelter in nearby Berea, which received him without enmity, but he stayed there only a short time, in sight of Greece by now.

Paul went alone to Athens, leaving his companions along the way to continue and complete his work. Now he made the rough model, and when he saw that the new church was taking shape, he entrusted it to disciples, so that they could bring it to perfection. He could trust them. Titus, Silvanus, and Timothy were eager and devoted workmen, and not a small part of Paul's creation was effected by those three faithful and industrious pupils, but they lived always in the immense shadow of their master, which spread out over the world to cover so much territory.

To Athens! There were very few Jews in Athens, but one could hardly not go there.

The sun of Greek civilization was by that time almost an extinguished star. The light radiating from that sun had been absorbed by the atmosphere around it. The beacon of poetry and art no longer burned on the hills of the Parthenon, but pale lunar reflections of the sun gleamed from the torches lit at Rome, at Alexandria, at Ephesus, and in other cities. The first splendor was long gone and another lesser age of splendor would be heralded in the century to come with Antony and Marcus Aurelius; but now, between the two great epochs, Athens was living the mediocre life of a provincial city. The heroes and poets had been succeeded by philosophers, and the philosophers by grammarians, rhetoricians, and fencing masters. Athens was now the city of schools and playing fields.

When a country is enriched by trade, art is impoverished. And now that trade was enriching Greece at Corinth, art in Athens had fallen on hard times. But though no longer great and illustrious, Athens was always an honored and respected city. Intractable with her conquerors and rather untrustworthy, all the soldiers who passed through her and lowered their arms in respectful obeisance, from Sulla to Caesar, Pompey to Octavius. No one dared to raise a hand against her monuments: instead they found it more delicate and more useful to ransack them. Small barbarian kings and magnificent mad emperors competed to pay her honor, sending their sons and poets to study at her schools.

From Athens the apostle went on to Corinth, from the decaying *grande dame,* he turned to the *nouveau riche* shopkeeper. Much easier to fight against the flesh in the corrupt cities than against the spirit in Athens: and Corinth was the most corrupt of the cities of the world. The flesh is weak and the enemy harbored in the spirit is untamable.

He stayed longer in Corinth than he had stayed in any other city up to now, twenty months. A sign that there was more labor, not easy but productive. The city is located between two seas, the Aegean on this side, the Ionian on the other. And beyond the Ionian was Italy. Certainly in his heart Paul felt the temptation to venture forth on that sea, but he was worried by words from the east. Almost as if the hand of an envious and evil Penelope were reaching out to undo the fragile material he was weaving with such effort. At Jerusalem it was easy to destroy the great absentee in public opinion. What was happening to him in Jerusalem was what happened to the Roman generals when they left the metropolis to conquer the world. Jerusalem was ungrateful: he must return to Jerusalem.

18

Philippi, The Beloved Church

Philippi was the city that Paul loved most of all, because it loved him most. The little community he gathered around him almost immediately became one which never gave him any trouble.

When a prisoner in Rome in later years, he will write a letter to the Philippians also, and there will blossom from his heart so unaccustomed to tender words of love, without a shadow of reproof or a drop of bitterness, words quivering with that secret weeping which never gushed from Paul's eyes, seared by the sun and unremitting labor. The words of recollection and advice used to these unforgettable friends are of incomparable sweetness: "Rejoice in the Lord always, again will I say it, rejoice."

The little church at Philippi helped him always, sending him aid wherever he was: and he accepted alms from them, while rejecting them from every other church. He made it a point of honor always to be able to support himself by his own work, and he said it and wrote it with an insistence which was self-respect and indirect reproof to him who does not do so: a weakness which must be permitted to truly strong men. With the Philippians he became humble and was happy to confess that he was a humble recipient of their generosity.

Since there were few Jews and no synagogue at Philippi, he gave his first speeches in the open air, in a natural chapel located on the bank of the River Ganga. Then his friends wanted him to speak in their houses, and his later speeches were made in friendly homes. From that moment he adopted a variation in his preaching which proved most efficacious, a form of conversation. Arguments that issue from the heart find their secret ways better than those that begin in the mind.

Women particularly listened to him, because women stay at home while men go out to work. Excluded from Christian preaching after the first years of open community, they re-entered by the gate of Philippi, and these Macedonian women friends were the apostle's most active assistants. How different are these active and alacritous Greek women from the contemplative Magdalen! Most of all Lydia, "the seller of purple," that is, the dye-merchant.

Lydia was a native of Thyatira in Lydia, the city renowned for its purple dye and cloth. Lydia may have taken her fame from her native land, and at Philippi, she conducted thriving trade in the precious cloth. More than anyone, she underwrote Paul's needs. After years have passed, many will forget the man who renewed their lives now that he is old and far away, and they are aged and disgraced by life's hardships: Lydia will never forget him, she who was the first Greek woman converted to Jesus by Paul.

And there were others. Women, like stern words spoken in an affectionate tone of voice, also like tender language said in a stern voice. Evodia and Syntyche were two tireless deaconesses, indefatigable to the point of rivalry. The young

Epaphroditus envied Timothy his intimacy with the master and tried to emulate him. In this affectionate company, Paul's words spread without encountering obstacles: the preacher became the persuasive and indulgent preceptor. The community was like one large family.

The good results he achieved without raising his voice disarmed the apostle of his stronger dialectic. In the Orient they regarded him as a rival and a rebel: here they considered him a friend and father. He did not need to resort to the severity and strictness of the tirade because he found obedience and sincere desire to believe in what he said. His sermons, which from the pulpit were usually a doctrinaire lesson, were here familiarized into informative conversation.

This was also the secret of the immediate adherence he achieved. The new religion was quickly understood from the heart when presented in the light of its great virtue, charity, love, and chastity. A train of good workers was called to Christ, and a sentiment of highest morality spread throughout the community, preventing jealousies and dissension.

In that city surrounded by tender green meadows, deep shady woods, and clear running water where flocks of sheep came down from the mountains to drink, Jesus' gospel was brought to a rapid flowering, and the stern Paul assumed an idyllic tone.

One incident interrupted him. An hysterical girl, a pythoness who went about predicting the future to the peasants, the poor servant of exploiting masters, ran into the missionaries of Jesus one day and left her trade to follow them, pleading and crying to them to take her with them because they were the true servants of the most high God and the heralds of the way of salvation. Paul exorcised the poor obsessed girl who was freed from the evil spirit and cured, and she too was ready to become an intrepid deaconess.

But her masters were ill-content because they saw great profits slipping from their hands. They seized Paul and Silas one day when they caught them alone and dragged them before the magistrates for judgment. Then, being Romans, they used the usual fawning pretexts and the words of cowardice of men without courage. "These men are convulsing our city; they are Jews and set forth customs which it is not lawful for us who are Romans to admit or practice." Acts 16:20-21.

And the Roman magistrates condemned the two law-breakers to the rods. Paul and Silas were stripped naked and subjected to the usual stripes, then, still bleeding, they were thrown into prison and the jailer was ordered to keep a good watch over them. To make this a guard of iron, he buried them in the most subterranean dungeon and chained their legs.

There was no escape: and yet they escaped. About midnight the two prisoners first prayed and then arose and sang praises of the Highest, and the others in the cells nearby listened to that sweet song. "Rise and pray," they sang. "Thus saith our fathers so that all the universe may cease at this hour for one instant and praise the Lord, and even the stars and the trees, and the rivers and the angels and the souls of the just. . . ."

And the final invocation resounded: "Marantha: Come, O Lord . . . the Lord will come. . . ."

A violent earthquake shook the earth. The foundations of the prison trembled, the walls cracked, the doors flew open, the chains of their leg-irons were loosened.

The jailer was jarred awake and seeing the door open, the prisoners free, he drew his sword to kill himself, fearing he would be punished with a more painful death. But from the depths of his cell, Paul cried to him to hold his hand: "Stop,

152

do thyself no harm; we are all here." Acts 16:28. The jailer lit the lantern, groped through the dark, and found the two Jewish prisoners. They could have fled, but they had not.

He was moved by such holiness and strength of soul. He led them into the light, knelt at their feet and begged them to teach him too the way of salvation. Then that very night he brought them to his own house. He washed the sores on their back and chests with warm water: he prepared something for them to eat; he asked that they baptize him too and his family; and since they wanted it, he brought them back to the prison.

What else had happened during that night besides the earthquake so that at break of day the magistrates sent the lictors to the prison with orders to free the two Jewish prisoners? Perhaps powerful friends of Paul had intervened, with money or other more honest arguments, to guarantee the prisoners' innocence. Perhaps the earthquake had disturbed the superstitious consciences of the judges, too ready to mete out stripes without trial. In a word, they ordered the prisoners freed.

The prisoners did not want to come out. Liberty was theirs by right, not as a concession to authority. Then Paul revealed to the jailer that they were Roman citizens. He said: "They have beaten us publicly without trial, we who are Romans, and have thrown us into prison; and would they now cast us out secretly? Not at all! Let them come themselves and lead us out."

It was a serious business. The jailer repeated Paul's words to the magistrates and they were terrified by them. Two Roman laws, a Valerian, and a Portian law passed centuries earlier, forbade punishing a Roman citizen without trial and enjoined severe penalties on transgressors of these laws. Paul was a man who clearly knew the laws of Rome.

It ended in the best of ways. The magistrates came to the

153

prison to ask the prisoners' pardon, then they had them brought to their houses with an escort of honor. Paul decided to leave the city, and another guard of honor escorted him to the gate. The one time he left a city without fleeing under a hail of threats and stones; however, he had been in danger of death. He was followed by Silas and Timothy. The doctor Luke stayed at Philippi where he already had patients. And he may have been the authoritative person who intervened with the magistrates.

19

"If Any Man Will Not Work, Neither Let Him Eat"

But if evangelization was easy at Philippi, there were many snares and obstacles at Thessalonica. Here there was a very important synagogue with many Jews; and complications naturally followed.

But this alternation of calm and stormy periods was good for Paul's restless spirit. An easy life might have dulled it, but the trials, the efforts, the sudden shocks honed his steely temper. He went from serene meditation to struggle and breathed deeply when he found himself in his element.

At Thessalonica Paul came face to face with the Greek world for the first time, for he had found only intimations of it at Philippi, which was more or less Roman, although a Romanism steeped in the ways of the east. The Greek spirit hovered over these terraced, open gardens in the shadow of Mount Olympus, although the Cyclopian walls and aqueducts were of Roman design.

Also of Roman origin was that heavy wind of millenary awaiting which already breathed over the empire. Evil days were upon it, for government was in the hands of a man not miserable but marrowless and of two women who mistook their wildest whims, their most brazen perversions, and their foulest ambitions for esthetic license.

The Jewish refugees banished by Claudius' edict brought with them to the Orient the terror and disgust now fermenting in Rome. Messalina and Agrippina and their ministers, freedmen, and relatives generated a universal dismay with their cruelties and contamination. In this climate agitated and oppressed imaginations fantasied the approach of the anti-Christ, the eve of the coming of the Lord.

It was the place and the hour for ardent preaching; after the quiet conversations at Philippi, exhortation and invective, diatribe and reproof. The huge and crowded synagogue was an ideal auditorium for Paul. He presented himself clothed in all his authority. And, as happened to him in the moments of severest struggle, his words were lifted to apocalyptic pitch. At Thessalonica especially he spoke of life beyond the tomb, of the Kingdom of Heaven, of Supreme ends, and his discourse often assumed an eschatological character. Consequently, he had a following of cultivated or intellectually curious men rather than housewives. A certain Jason, a good-hearted Jew with an Hellenic name, wanted him in his own house, and Paul accepted his hospitality since the wealthy Jason was a tent merchant and Paul could repay his obligation by weaving cloth in his shop.

When, shortly afterward, he wrote his first letter to the Thessalonicans, he would remember this labor of his joyous pride. "Whereas we might have claimed honor as missionaries of Christ: but we became babes in the midst of you: yearning over you like a nurse cherishing her children." He had not wanted to be a burden and had humbled himself out of his great love for them.

On three consecutive Sabbath days Paul spoke in the synagogue and he always had a crowded and attentive audience. They were not only the disappointed and afflicted poor, but also the well-to-do and powerful. As the evangelization passed from the Oriental world to the Greco-Roman world it rose, step by step, from the pariahs toward the privileged. The historian of the Acts says: "Great multitudes of proselytes and Gentiles gathered together, and also not a few matrons."

Therefore, Paul had a particular penchant for this church. He remembered the community of men and women friends at Philippi with sorrowful nostalgia, and he loved the community above all; but the church of Thessalonica stayed at the summit of his thoughts as his most solid construction, and it was formed in only a few months. He never praised another church the way he praised this one: for constancy, faithfulness, and the brethren's mutual love. Restless but strong, with some frenzies which were immediately followed by reform, he considered it the model of his churches, and he often presented it to the others as an example. He had realized his ideal.

Because the tree was laden with fruit, the stone throwing began. A crowd was aroused against the messianic revolutionary. They used the servile weapon of denunciation to the authorities, the synod's weapon against Jesus. "He's a traitor, an enemy of Caesar!" To accuse Paul of sedition to the Roman state was the quickest way of being rid of him. This messianic missionary proclaimed a certain Jesus was the King and not Caesar, the only king of the world, like the synod's accusation against Jesus to Pilate.

They surrounded Jason's house so that the culprit could not

flee, and took it by assault. It was a mob of vagabonds swept from the slums, putting the city into an uproar to seize three unarmed men. Paul and his companions were not found, however; either they were not there or were able to flee by a secret exit. Then the mob seized Jason and some of the brethren and dragged them before the patriarchs. "These men, who have turned the world upside down, are here also, and Jason is their host. All these men are acting contrary to Caesar's decrees, saying that there is another King, one Jesus."

The magistrates were people who wanted to see the matter clearly. They realized that it was a question of spiritual not temporal matters, and that there was no cause for fear. Therefore, they asked Jason to send his undesirable guests away and made him deposit a sum of money as a bond. But this time there was neither prison nor thrashing.

If Jason and the other brethren had not advised the apostle to remove himself from the scene, there might have been a riot of the infuriated mob. The Church at Thessalonica was founded now, and there were convinced and resolute men to defend it: he could carry the word farther—into Greece!

They supplied him and his two young companions with bread for the journey and accompanied them part of the way on the Via Ignazia.

Before going down into Achaia, Paul decided to make a journey into the interior and stop in Berea, a not large city which had, however, many Jews and an important synagogue. Although by now experience should have dissuaded him, here too, faithful to his system, he wanted to begin with the Jews. It could have been good diplomacy to support his change of direction with the evidence of his failure with the Jews, but it was also love for his own people and their history. A family of converted Greeks or Asiatics made him proud in his mind, but a family of converted Jews made his heart joyful. The pupils whom he loved above all, as a father loves his sons, were the Jews.

At Berea he found a colony more disposed to heed him than the one at Thessalonica. As the sons of Israel went farther away from the fetters of Jerusalem and closer toward the climate of Greece and Rome, ventilated by so many currents, they were enlarged by the exposure to a different climate and became more broad-minded and curious about new things. At Berea the greater part of the Jews worked in the mines, but there were also people of means. Here, too, a Christian church was established next to the synagogue. Here, too, a young enthusiast, Sopater, entered Paul's life, as Aristarchus, Gaius, and Secundus had entered it at Thessalonica.

But not even at Berea was life tranquil. Though the local Jews who were not converted remained calm, those at Thessalonica envied him his easy victory at Berea. They sent agitators to stir up the people, and the usual uproar followed. The brethren saved their master, then they persuaded him to leave, entrusting him to robust bodyguards who would be able to defend him. The journey to Athens was completed by way of the sea, with a swing around the island of Euboea.

Silvanus and Timothy stayed at Berea. Then, from Berea, they returned to Thessalonica.

It was the first time Paul came to a new and great city alone. If he left his most trusted disciples behind, it means that he had assigned a task to them. It was necessary to put some last touches to his construction. These churches in Macedonia had been born in a few months, and they were dear to his heart because they sprang up in the heat of enthusiasm, but he had not had time to see how that incandescent material would

159

stand up when the flame was withdrawn. In a year, Silas and Timothy would bring him bad news.

It was not a question of cooling of affections but of doctrinal dissension. Doubts and disagreements arose, especially in Thessalonica, on how to interpret Paul's ideas on certain particulars which had remained obscure since the apostle had not had time to clarify them.

Then Paul wrote two letters which the disciples brought to the favorite church. They are the first two of Paul's letters which have been left to us. They are also the earliest portions of the New Testament, written in the year 53 A.D. After twenty years the doctrines of Jesus are transferred from oral tradition to the written word.

The controversy among the Thessalonican faithful was over the moment of the rebirth, the second coming of Christ, which many believed and hoped to be imminent. Paul tried to dissuade them from this belief and this hope. He wrote words which he had certainly already said in person: that no one knew the time of the second coming and the day of the Lord comes suddenly like a thief in the night. Jesus, too, had said the same. These elementary words, however, were wrapped in a severe aura of admonition, more likely to give rise to dismay than conviction.

But there were other more comforting words added to these sombre-hued ones. The rather comfortable belief in the imminence of the Lord's return had been used as an excuse for relaxation in the spiritual activity of the faithful, as always happens when the human soul is troubled by the insidious sense of the provisory. This news particularly afflicted Paul and he took up his pen to give his Macedonian brethren a moral lesson, which could be more easily understood than a theological one.

In the second letter he wrote: "Now we charge you, brethren, in the name of the Lord Jesus Christ to withdraw yourselves from every brother that is disorderly, and walketh not according to the tradition which ye received from us. For yourselves know how ye ought to imitate us, in that we were not disorderly whilst with you, neither did we take food unearned at any man's hand, but we worked night and day in toil and struggle, that we might not burden any of you; not that we have not the right so to do, but we wished to furnish in ourselves a pattern for you to imitate."

Enjoining honesty and loyalty in business, he made an announcement which was both a promise and a threat. "It is a just thing before God to give tribulations to those who give you tribulations."

And he added the terrible admonishment which reverberates down the centuries: "If any man will not work, neither let him eat."

20

The False and Lying Gods

Alone in Athens, Paul felt the weight of his solitude and could not adapt to it. After several months, he still complained: "I am alone in Athens, alone and lost." He who loved solitude: for what reason, for what purpose, did he want to be alone this time? He had told the brethren at Berea to send Timothy and Silas to him soon, but it is certain that he had sought this solitude intentionally.

And solitude it was, undisturbed by encounters and contacts. Athens was an extinguished city, but it would have been a heap of ashes for Paul even in its most resplendent and liveliest epoch, so much was it a city foreign to his spirit. He looked toward the West because the world to be conquered was in the West, but his mental orientation was rigidly Semitic, with only a slight yeast of the Hellenist and Tarsian schools, and he was truly lost in this pleasant way of living, easy and serene, which was the felicity of the Greeks.

The inimitable grace of everything in the city—works of art, schools, and altars, philosophical discussions and athletic games—was as nothing to his agitated soul of stoic passions and ideas. The Greek genius had formerly been filled with mysterious anguish and a sense of epic fate and tragedy and was never happily serene save in its sculpture, but now it seemed to elude the sense of death and willingly surrendered to a light and fresh joy of living. Paul had death and sorrow hewed into his every thought; they were woven into all his religious and moral propaganda, even if death was then followed by resurrection.

Of the ancient heroic virtues, of the poetry and political wisdom which had been the glory of its fathers, only a facile and polite skepticism remained to the Athenians of Paul's day. Their philosophy was frayed by eclecticism, and they had a joyless irony of the kind already heralded by Lucian. It was the state of mind most detested and censured by the apostle.

All the same, not every fruit of the great and ancient plant was rotten. The best of time past now gathered in the Stoic, and certainly Paul did not dislike that severe and honest ethic. He did not deny the spiritual thread which had had its beginning in Pythagoras, which was to pass through Heraclitus, Socrates, Plato, and Aristotle to bind him too: the tireless research into first causes, the origin of every living thing, the anxiety for the unique and universal being which created the world and governs it. Through this religious philosophy, the human soul had risen step by step toward the God of the Christians. But it is also the destiny of every philosophy that, brought to the supreme degree of completion and perfection, it harbors within itself the germs of indifference. In every ripeness, there is the beginning of decomposition. Except that in the disintegration of the great Mediterranean philosophy there had survived the ferments and intimations of the new religion which he, Paul, was announcing to the world.

He went all along through the city's streets, for he had come here not so much to teach as to observe, listen, and learn. He knew that his teaching would not find pupils. He wanted an audience of uneducated and ignorant people, not of knowing and educated ones. "If any thinks he knows something, he has not yet known as one needs to know." It was useful to be alone, to observe and listen, isolated from the varied conversation of his companions, spared the annoyances of useless acquaintances. In the midst of the agora crowded with poets and idlers, he too seemed a vagabond. The urchins of the street followed him hooting and jeering.

The great poets of Rome had come here to seek inspiration among the Parthenon's white columns and immortal memories, just as the Italian poets of the heroic romanticism went to Sante Croce in Florence. Paul roamed about among the columns and hermae, from an oration in the forum he went to a fencing field, testing the solidity of his thinking in the impact with this culture, for him ephemeral, for the others eternal. He wanted to know the others' ideas on the mystery of being, the better to prove the incorruptibility of his own. He retempered, sharpened, and made more lucid the truth of his God in friction against the false and lying gods.

Certainly Athens could not speak to him with a loving voice or ask of him words of love, insensitive as he was to the plastic beauty, disinterested in all the figurative arts. The genius of perfect form was repugnant to the iconoclastic spirit of the son of Israel: there was almost a kind of incompatibility which intervened in him between pure aesthetic enjoyment and warm human emotions, or at least the ecstacy of the mind, for the spirit weakens the eyes' visual joy in form. Though affections burned to an incandescent state of passion in him, the pleasing illusions of the senses were foreign to his life, despotically dominated by thought. Every divination of his soul was subordinated and obedient to that Master, so absolute it gave him no respite.

But now the genius of form too had been banned from the city which had first nursed it. The Parthenon still bloomed intact, the white celestial flower on the terrestrial Acropolis, and the city was adorned with other marvelous temples, with other monuments and theatres and porticos. The Phidian Pallas Athena and other gods and goddesses filled the temples, monuments, theatres, and porticos with incomparable marble statues. But in the midst of them, in humiliation and offense to such beauty, the new conquerors had tossed in formless heaps of their own numerous herd, an unseemly crown of deified images. Sulla, Caligula, Julius and Livy had come from Rome to mingle with Apollo, Ares, Aphrodite, and Athena. There was also Brutus, liberty's friend and Augustus' enemy; because the Athenian people had wanted him. Cicero would have liked to be there, but he was not. Petronius was wont to say that it was easier to meet a god in Athens than a man.

Jesus had said to the women of Samaria, "The day will come when neither on this mountain nor in Jerusalem will you adore the true God."

There was a synagogue too in Athens, but of what use was a synagogue in Athens? There was a quarter entirely occupied by Jews, the Keromeikos: it was a colony of potters, industrious artisans in the midst of a rather lazy people, and their modest needs contrasted with the decadent and spendthrift esthetes around them. But Paul rarely went to these potters of his own people and spoke only occasionally in the synagogue, with little enthusiasm and no success. Timothy came to join him outside the Keromeikos, in lonely spots of great trees and wandering crowds.

166

The trees, at least, were restful after the oppression of all those stones. The seeker of spiritual beauty, out of place among those worshippers of pure form, found that supreme good among the sideral heights of his thinking. Perhaps he poured out his inner bitterness in confidences to the young companion finally arrived to sustain him. "These Greeks, Timothy, were a people of pleasant fantasies and they fashioned a certain number of deities for themselves as one fashions the various characters of a comedy, without ever truly believing in them. They neither feared, nor loved, nor even respected them as one respects Him who has created us. Where fear and respect are lacking, the comedy ends as farce, children who knead clay puppets for the joy of breaking them. They make them great in marble—colossal—but tiny, tiny, in their hearts. They amuse themselves by dismantling the mechanical contrivances of their puppets. They said they adored them, but were ever ready to cover them with insults. Their love, if such there ever was, was never as disinterested as the love of God must be. They directed prayers to them, but they knew it was necessary to put their hands in their purses if they wanted to obtain favors, to pay for heavenly benefits. They had recourse to their purses and to their knives. They slaughtered their daughters and their sisters, sometimes merely in the hope of winning an unjust war. Oh, our own Hebrew fathers had these faults too, it's true! If the gods permitted themselves to withhold their favors, it was too bad; the men raised their hands even against their own gods, who ran away! Immortal and omnipotent gods, but not courageous. They were captured in battle. A god wounded and stamped on by a man, Timothy! And they were like men, these gods, in fact like magpies; they yelled with pain and terror. If there had at least been agreement among them as befits the rulers of the world! But those deities shaped by the poets' fantasy spent their idleness in discord, intrigue, and squabbles. They attacked each

167

other treacherously, they pulled each other's hair and expressed themselves in a language of drunkards, servants, and prostitutes. The Olympic assemblies were such as to ennoble political conventions. They had no shame about washing the dirty linen of their treachery and cowardice in public. They played every kind of practical joke on each other. They went into heat over any little female or fancily dressed fop, like stallions in the month of May. The male gods, satiated with celestial quail, sought females of human flesh for their extravagant pleasures and the female gods opened the celestial alcoves to men of human flesh. Delightful amusing spectacles, lightsome fantasies, Timothy, but the soul comes away sickened. This has always happened, from the time of Homer, at least once as an exception, but now it becomes a normal daily occurrence. The true God and concept of the poets and philosophers tried to bring back the sentiment of mystery to the human soul, but they found no response among the thoughtless people; in fact the religious disorder increased. Now other deities, male and female, natives of Egypt, Persia, and Syria, have come to mingle with the gods of Athens, Thebes, and Sparta who live on Mount Olympus. And now the emperors have decided that they too must have altars and victims; together, gods and emperors, they make a happy carnival. Finally, as there can sometimes be a spiritual wisdom of the flesh, so there is often a carnal heaviness of the spirit. Now, Timothy, those who still believe make no difference in their prayers and their statues, their verse and their curses, between Zeus and Serapis, between Ares and Caesar, between Aphrodite and a courtesan, between Athena and a horse, between Hermes and a lackey. . . ."

They took Paul too for a god, a foreign god come to meddle in Athenian affairs. People heard him speak one day in the

Forum and retained only two strange words, hitherto unheard in the Greek language, of his difficult discourse, the words "Jesus" and "Resurrection." They thought that "Jesus" and "Resurrection" were two new gods, male and female, the most recent arrivals from the East, and that he, the speaker, if not a god, was certainly a messenger, a demi-god profoundly initiated into the abstruse mystery. Loose talk. But what did he want, where did he come from?

He was asked to speak in a meeting on the Areopagus, the Hill of Ares, to expound his theories to a group of wise men. This was an audience different from the usual one. These gracious and well-educated persons were not intolerant; they did not become heatedly angry at people who had ideas unlike their own; they gave hospitality to all opinions because they gave importance to none. Stoics and epicureans met together to listen to the iconoclast's words.

As he had been going that morning from Athena's altar, where he usually stopped to watch an ewer burning olive oil, toward the altar of mercy which was his usual goal because of that great Christian name, Paul had come upon an ara dedicated "To the Unknown God," which was in the most ancient traditions of Greek mythology. He had taken the starting point of his speech from it, though he certainly prepared the speech in his mind some time before. Studying, observing, and listening, he had realized that his speech must be organized differently here. You could not speak to wise men of Athens as he usually spoke to the simple artisans and impassioned souls. Christianity is not built on a public made up of men of letters, but these literary men were also "seekers of God" and as such he would praise them. The Socratic demon had become conscience in Menander, and the Stoic enjoined his listeners to heed the voice of conscience. Therefore, he decided to give the Athenian sages

169

his own kind of philosophy lesson, because philosophy is worth nothing without religious spirit and the search after truth in the mystery. He said:

. . . Men of Athens, I behold you in all respects not a little religious. For as I was passing along and noticing the objects of your worship, I found also an altar bearing the inscription 'To the Unknown God.' What therefore ye worship in ignorance, that I proclaim to you. 'God, who made the world and all things therein, He, being Lord of heaven and earth,' dwelleth not in temples made with hands, neither hath He need of aught that He should be served by human hands, seeing that Himself 'giveth' to all life and 'breath' and all things. Yea, from one man He hath made the whole human race to dwell upon the entire face of the earth, determining their appointed seasons and the boundaries of their abode, that they should seek God, if haply groping after Him they might find Him. Not that He is far from any one of us; for in Him we live and move and have our being, as also some of your poets have said, for we are His very offspring. Being therefore the offspring of God, we ought not to think that the divine is like to gold or silver or stone, to aught graven by art and invention of man. Such times of ignorance God hath overlooked, but doth now declare to men that all are everywhere to repent, inasmuch as He hath appointed a day whereon He is about 'to judge the world with justice' by the man whom He hath determined, giving proof thereof to all by raising him from the dead.

At this point, he could not continue. The speech had been modest enough in its oratorical efficacy. The apostle's eloquence flamed with excitement, but in the presence of such an assemblage he studied his words one by one, and they were cooled in preparation. To unbridle himself, he needed the whiplash; he was disarmed by calm and lack of interruption. And yet his thoughts emerged clearly and sharply in the few words he said. Perhaps if he had been able to continue, the contained beginning would have been followed by an impassioned flight.

But it did not follow, because they would not let him continue. His Greek, tolerable elsewhere, must have seemed most incorrect to the purists of the Stoa. The epicureans laughed when he came to the Resurrection, or the exotic goddess Anastasis the way they interpreted it. They went away, amused and skeptical. They told him to go home. With the slyly patronizing air people use to a deluded innocent, someone said "We'll listen to you another time."

He had been beaten before the battle was begun. But he expected it because he knew that the pride harbored in the spirit is much harder to fight than the weak yielding flesh. And he folded his tents to go and fight the flesh at Corinth.

There were a few disciples left from the Athenian failure and they escorted him toward the isthmus. Denis, a member of the Areopagus, and a woman named Damaris, are recorded, but they are only a fleeting memory.

21

Paul and Women

Paul arrived at Corinth with the onset of autumn. It had been a torrid summer, and he had suffered much alone at Athens. He was not worn out by his mission, but by the disillusionment which had aggravated the physical effects of the heat. At Corinth, he was reborn, because in just a few days he could foresee the good work that awaited him. Immediately, he realized that here there was a much greater field of action open to him.

He had embarked at Piraeus and left ship at Cenchrea, the city's port on the Aegean Sea: there was another port on the Ionian side of the gulf. Between these two ports swarmed a heterogeneous population from the very rich to the penniless— merchants, sailors, slaves, and loose women—all busily engaged with their affairs.

This was the other face of Greece too. A few miles away from Athens, Corinth was an entirely different city. Fallen into Roman hands a century and a half before Christ, she was first destroyed, then reconstructed, and nothing remained of those ancient monuments which Athens had conserved in its museum except the atmosphere of the city. But Athens was growing old in contemplation of her memories while Corinth seethed with avid and disorderly youthfulness. As the mind becomes barren in indolence and irony, so the flesh becomes swollen and corrupt in measureless desire.

In the two ports merchandise of every sort, not excluding human flesh, was deposited from East and West. And from one side and the other, vices and perversions poured out. Where swarms of sailors starve from their long fast from land, the wharves and alleys are a rabbit warren of poor women in search of buyers. Where gross merchants retire to count their treasures, courtesans flock like flies on filth. The name of Corinth had become a synonym for vice: verbs, adjectives, and adverbs were derived from it. Everyone knew what a Corinthian girl and the Corinthian ill were. And the word Corinthisize was used for every obscene act.

Pandemian Aphrodite was the protectress of the city. She had her temple on the Acrocorinthus, and several thousands of priestesses in attendance.

Riches were heaped up, but around those heaps was the squalor of blackest misery. Someone has said there were almost half a million slaves, but it must be an exaggerated figure. Certainly misery and slavery generated crime. When, in a few years, Paul writes a letter of rebuke to the riotous Corinthians, he will discharge a cannonload of terrible qualifications: adulterers, fornicators, idolators, effeminates, thieves, cheats, drunkards, railers. His preaching at Corinth had, above all, a moral intention to make clear that life is to be taken seriously.

There was a large colony of Jews, but they too must have been people of few scruples, living as it were in a society which had no scruples of any sort. When Paul arrived there, anti-

Semitism was beginning to make itself felt too. Among the Jews were many converts to Christianity.

Paul found friends in one of these converted families, a husband and wife called Aquila and Prisca, or Priscilla. Since they too were tent merchants and had opened a booth in the city, he could find work there. They had come from Rome, along with many others dispersed by the persecution of Claudius. The husband was a native of Pontius who had emigrated to Rome to follow his trade: the wife a Roman gentlewoman, perhaps of the Cornelius family. He was a good worker, a man who knew his trade; but the administrator and organizer of the shop was his wife, an educated and able woman.

They were pleasant and useful company, even though it may have pricked Paul's self-esteem to know that the new religion was already being spread in Rome, the capital of the Gentiles, while he, Apostle to the Gentiles, had not yet been there. Fortunately his present work, which was intense and effective, distracted him from any such regrets.

Since the Jews who crowded the synagogue were many, there were numerous adherents to the new Christian church, inside and outside the synagogue. It was not calm, never peaceable, and always highly disordered, but the importance the Corinthian church quickly assumed over all the other churches founded by Paul was due in a large part to this perpetual restlessness. The discord, brought about by its numbers, became a new source of importance.

Paul repeated the gesture of Pisidian Antioch at Corinth: shaking the dust from his garments, he passed from the synagogue to the Gentiles. For the Gentiles, Paul did what he usually left to the elders of the new church: he baptized many with his own hands. The first days he was alone, having sent Timothy to Thessalonica; then Timothy rejoined him and with him

175

came Silas, who had remained behind. The two young men aided their master.

Many are the new believers in Corinth whose name is recorded by history; those who have been forgotten must be considerably more. There were Stephenas, Gaius, Achaicus, Fortunatus, a Hebrew jurist named Zena, Erastus (who was a very powerful man because he was city treasurer), Chloe, a rich widow, and all the servants of her household, and the deaconess of Cenchrea, the faithful Phoebe. Titius, called the Just, one of the leaders who was also one of Paul's first converts, offered him hospitality and paid him honor in his own house, which was next to the synagogue. The president of the synagogue, Crispus, followed Titius' example: there was a great scandal among the Pharisees on the day Crispus left the Jews for the Gentiles. Sosthenes, Crispus' successor, may also have been inclined toward Christianity. And other nests of Christians must have sprung up here and there in Achaea and the Peloponnesus. Paul stayed in Corinth almost two years, and during such a long stay we can presume that he left the city to go to Olympia or Argus or Sparta; if not he, then some of his pupils.

At this point, some feminine faces reappear on the scene of the new religion. With the growing number of women and their consequent activities, Paul thought that they too might be cautiously admitted to the liturgical life of the new church. The Hebrew Mosaic Law had always excluded them; and the church at Jerusalem, bound to that law, hesitated to admit them. Paul had never opposed the law in this, and he did not even have the hesitations of those at Jerusalem. His severe disposition did not permit the relaxation in religious practices which might have derived from feminine company. While the other apostles took wives and sisters with them, it seemed to Paul only a vanity and a distraction. He took advantage of every occasion to reprove the brethren's customs with subtle allusions. It was a militant mission, and the militia must be a thoroughly manly army; in words as well as deeds. The sturdy Roman woman, Priscilla, was never called Priscilla by him, but always Prisca, without the more affectionate diminutive.

But now he decided to try admitting women. Devoted companions, helpful sisters, these he had had before in Asia and in Macedonia, and especially in Lydia, but he had always left them to the cares of housekeeping. Now he thought they had acquired the right to enter into the liturgy, and the Church was now ready to receive them.

No scandal followed. From Philippi to Thessalonica, from Thessalonica to Berea, from Berea to Corinth, we see more and more the gentle, feminine features coming to light among the men. As long as Paul was present with his example and his all-seeing gaze, the conduct of the Christian community, even in this most ill-conducted city, did not become spoiled. Days of peace were not lacking in the midst of struggle, and then life flowed limpid and free, fed by a spring of serene joy. The family feeling which had always been so strong among the Jews was revivified in the Christian community. The chaste delights of modesty refined femininity in faith, and almost sanctified it.

Now the rite of Eucharist was no longer celebrated every day, but only once a week. Sunday, the day of the Lord, was chosen, because on that day Jesus had risen, and on that day the Lord had rested after the creation of the world. And the weekly meeting assumed greater importance. In the divine service, *Irene,* peace, was added to *Agape,* love, and one poured into the cup of wine, the other into tepid water. Music, songs, and dances followed a joyous meal and the prayer. The most beautiful songs were born, and they added their own suggestive power to the persuasive efficacy of words: they will easily become the surest viaticum of the faith and will accompany its growth. The aspirations of the spirit found musical expression. Some of these songs were written by Paul.

A fragment of one of them is: "He is with us throughout our journey, the Savior who gives life and does not deny our souls, the Man who was humbled and exalted by His trial. The Son of the Highest appears in the perfection of His Father, and the light radiates from the Word which was already in Him. He is truly the Messiah and was known before the creation of the world, so that He could save our souls forever by the truth of His Name. A new song rises from those who love Him. Hallelujah!"

The limpid voices of women and boys were specially trained in song, and for this reason too women were admitted to the liturgy. Then, as often happens when a finger is given and the whole hand is taken, the women began to take liberties which Paul had not granted. One tried to present herself at the gatherings with her head uncovered, and then Paul raised his voice: "No!" The woman must veil her head out of respect for the angels. Angels too can fall into temptation at the sight of fair female tresses and neglect their office, which is to bring God the prayers of the saints.

Later, toward the end of his life, when sad news of the corruption of his churches came to afflict him in his final prison, Paul will thunder terrible words against women: "The women are likewise to wear seemly apparel, with modesty and self-control, not adorning themselves with plaits, or gold, or pearls, or costly raiment, but (as befitteth women professing godliness) with good works. Let a woman learn quietly, with entire submission. Do not allow a woman to teach, or to have the mastery over a man: she is to be quiet."

Then came the day when the wind turned in Corinth too, and Paul was dragged like a criminal before the Roman tribunal.

Junius Annaeus Gallio was the proconsul at that time. He was loved and admired by contemporary historians as the most honorable of gentlemen, a man with the best of hearts, and modern historians too proclaim him one of the most educated and amiable men of his time. Seneca's younger brother, educated at the same school as Seneca, would also die a suicide by Nero's order. His older brother, who adored him wrote: "No man can be as good to a friend as Gallio is to all."

On this occasion the exemplary man did not behave very differently from Pontius Pilate twenty years earlier at Jerusalem. The complainers here were not only disillusioned Jews, as at Thessalonica, but were also pagans, pouring out their old anti-Semitism on this illustrious scapegoat.

The accusation leveled against Paul was the usual: disobedience to the Mosaic Law, because he preached of a God not acknowledged by that law. Gallio listened patiently to the accusers; then at the point where the apostle rose to reply, he took the word away from him, concluding the debate with a sharp cut. "If there had been some misdemeanor or serious crime in question, O Jews, I should with reason have borne with you; but if these are questions of word and of names of your law, ye must look to it yourselves. I have no mind to be judge of these things."

He did not condemn Paul, but he did not absolve him either. He spared him prison and the rods, but he abandoned him to the retaliation of his accusers. Paul must now decide to leave.

Meanwhile news arrived of dissension within the Thessalonican church, and a little time went by while he wrote the letters which Timothy would bear to those unruly brethren.

The young secretary was also the amanuensis of the letters, which Paul dictated and then signed with his own hand. The great missionary's first two writings were brief, almost as if their author were frightened by the solemn act he was engaged in accomplishing, the unusual authority he was taking on himself. It was customary and the prerogative of the Sanhedrin to communicate in writing with the synagogues scattered throughout the world: he was apostle but not the head and was usurping the power of the head of the Church. But he had begun, and other letters would follow, ever more complex, more eloquent, and more authoritative.

He could have gone personally to Thessalonica, but a journey to Macedonia was like taking the road of return and, on the shores of the gulf, he kept his eyes fixed on the vision of Rome. Only it became necessary to renounce Rome. The other news that reached him, from Jerusalem, also became more worrisome, and these were not yet controversies to be settled with a letter. So far away, rumor passed from mouth to mouth and swelled like a tempest. Termites were gnawing at the foundation of the edifice he was so painfully constructing, stone on stone.

The absent are always wrong, sad old verity of our sad old world. He could not go to Rome. The good captain does not venture forth on new conquests if the rear is unsafe and sedition cuts his supplies behind him. He also thought, though certainly unwillingly, that it was not his principle to invade the field sowed by others but to keep to the cultivation of his own.

He was returning from the most fruitful of his missions, but he was ill-content.

22

The Wondrous Vision

He boarded ship at Cenchrea with his disciples, and Aquila and Priscilla decided to go too. They were honest people; their trade, honestly exercised, did not prosper in a city already cluttered with traffic. Perhaps only Timothy remained to watch over the churches of Macedonia and Achaia. Their trip would have been pleasanter by land, where Paul had dear friends awaiting him whom he wanted to see again, but there was no time to lose. His sleepless nights were wracked by fears and misgivings.

Before he left he had had his already partly-bald head shaven clean, as prescribed by the Law to one who takes the Nazarene vow. He was going to Jerusalem in the guise of a penitent, to beg relief for his afflictions. Besides the worries that destroyed his sleep, his old ills came back periodically to torment him. That life of renunciations, fasts, and fatigues was not designed to heal his poisoned blood.

The ship touched at Ephesus, and officials of the synagogue, curious to see him and contradict him, invited him to stop.

Aquila and Priscilla remained there to seek better fortune than they had found at Corinth, but he did not because he wanted to go on to Jerusalem. He stopped only a few days, and one of them being a Saturday, he made a speech in the synagogue and then departed.

But the sun did not shine for him on the hills of Zion. He was chilled by the uncaring and suspicious coolness around him. He came with his spirit warmed and overflowing with a joy he wanted to impart to the leaders of the mother church, by telling them of the great works accomplished in three years of missions among the lands of the infidels. But they listened to him with uncordial expressions, with hostility and reproof. The first time he had come back, with Barnabas, after Cyprus and Galatia, they were more friendly, or had known better how to dissimulate their enmity. Now it seemed to him that they had convened to listen not to the victor bringing back the gift of his victory but to a wrongdoer in the act of exculpating an accused, himself. Paul recognized that the fears and suspicions which had wracked him and driven him to return were about to be verified.

It is the fate of all compromises that they never content any side but resolve into ephemeral truce. A ferment of bitterness rests in everyone, and it acidifies the disagreement into hate. The one and the other of the pacified signers consider themselves beaten, and they profit from the truce only to prepare for revenge.

They had marked out the limits of his preaching for Paul but, in truth, he had forgotten about them. He had letters of credential in his pocket but, since he attached no particular importance to them, his Pharisee enemies could give credence to the slander which reported that he had never had them. He had agreed to insist that the Gentiles would observe certain restrictions of the Mosaic Law, with the exception of the in-

182

admissible circumcision, but in practice he left them free to follow their usual customs outside the church, saving his severity for moral education and the practice of the virtues essential to the good Christian. They too were in the Law (the Ten Commandments, for example), and for them the Law was to be respected. But every other formal and ritualistic precept had no value after Jesus, no reason to exist, and were only empty shells. As he went farther away from Jerusalem, he went further away from the Law, shrugging off its useless weight.

The leaders at Jerusalem could not do this. Living in Israel's capital, the old law of Israel must retain all its dominion over them. Above all, the later-added zealots and pedants would not permit it; they had already infected the new religion with their own politics. The musty old air of the Temple was harmful to those who had to breathe it every day. No longer did the echoes of Jesus' strong words against false believers and whited sepulchers resound under the porticoes. As he grew older the ninety-year-old James had become more and more unbending in his wary conservatism. The Wise, the Just, the Bulwark of the Faith could not abdicate his task as bulwark against the assaults of revolution. He may have thought that revolution is brought in an organism's ripe years, to renew it, and feared that an organism still so weak and tender as the newborn religion would not be able to sustain the impact. With that sense of responsibility which is also wisdom, he wanted to proceed cautiously, but his caution became partisanship in those who followed him.

Moreover, doubts and uncertainties were to continue for a long time; three and a half centuries must go by before Saint Augustine makes the doubting Marcellinus understand how God had abrogated the ancient Mosaic law with the New Testament, because the common saying that "what was once well done, must not change is not true. The times have their own reasons."

The news about Paul's activities that reached James and the other leaders was certainly deformed by distance and the partisan interpretation of those who repeated it. We all know that the members of a herd tell the leaders only what they want to know, and that they tell it in such a way as to make it unpleasant. Many people stood to gain by putting Paul in a bad light. He had humbled too many ambitious men and had thrown out too many inept ones, so that there were many now who wanted to enjoy seeing him disgraced.

They began by whispering small slanderous remarks to one another, which swelled in sound and became accusations and calumnies as they circulated among the assembly. They may have requested James and the other elders to issue a circular letter disapproving Paul's actions, to put the faithful on guard against the soft words of the subverters. After all, the intruder was completely unscrupulous about taking a liberty never granted to him. The last-arrived had wanted to be the first, and he had succeeded; now he claimed to be the only one—he who had never seen Jesus, never heard His divine words, never loved and served Him. His intolerant ways were really becoming intolerable. The preacher was a perturber. The revolutionary was turning into a dictator, a despot. And he was a dictator who, as is the way of dictators, together with the oppression of other people's spirits, permitted himself pleasures.

Once the machine of calumny is put in action, there is no longer any evidence of truth that will chain its wheels, and political pharisaism is the great dissolvent of religion.

The greater part of the zealot emissaries who wandered about the environs of Jerusalem were poor and unemployed people who lived at the church's expense. Since they knew that Paul refused all aid and made a boast of this—a boast which irritated and humiliated them—it was natural to accuse him of living an exactly opposite life, one of distraction and ease.

Disinterest is a serious fault in the eyes of interested parties. Those women who followed him so fervently, and at whose hospitable houses he slept, some of them matrons and others fallen women, came close to being accused of being his intimates, and the severe words he preached were only his spiritual alibi. It was rumored that Thecla, on his account, left her betrothed on the eve of marriage; and that Lydia fed him with bread and more.

From malice to malice, it was easy enough for the apostle to become an imposter, an actor, a corruptor of conscience, an enemy of Christianity. And was the imposter really a Jew? He didn't happen to be a pagan who had had himself circumcised to marry the High Priest's daughter, only to have her father refuse him? This explained his aversion to circumcision. . . .

Peter had offended him in the church at Antioch, he had "withstood him to the face" with biting words; but Peter had pardoned the offense, remembering his Master's teaching, and for love of Jesus he would have presented the other cheek to the offender if occasion arose. He never retained a shadow of rancor against his great rival and continued to consider him the legitimate Apostle to the Gentiles, as he was the Apostle to the Jews.

Great schisms have always had their origin in small personal frictions. A great schism did not occur after this clash between Paul and Jerusalem, but the seed of the heresies that spring up in all the Eastern churches within a half century can be found in it.

The uncompromising Pharisees had been converted to Christianity without real conviction and had remained incorrigibly zealous and nationalistic; they understood the Messiah in the flesh better than the Messiah in the spirit and made religion into a political arm, not wanting to share the

Kingdom of Heaven nor the kingdom on earth with others.

The discord between Paul and the Church at Jerusalem could not be healed by a simple compromise which only regulated certain formal aspects of his activity as apostle. The fact that the leaders of that church had seen Jesus alive in human life and Paul had known Him only risen to eternal life lay at the base of their theological indifference. The disciples of Galilee could not erase the gentle Master from their memories, who was like them in His body and His needs, who dressed in the same kind of clothes, shared their bread, spoke their language, and like them slept and prayed. Now they knew that He was God but they could not forget that for three years they had thought Him a man and that belief remained to upset their thoughts. Jesus was Aramaic, Jesus was circumcised, Jesus had never disobeyed the Law, only perfected it. For Paul, Jesus was only the Christ, God. Not only the Son of the Father, but the Father Himself. As such He had appeared to him in the lightning flash on the road to Damascus, as such He had reappeared in dreams and visions and inspired him with thoughts, acts, and words. He had learned from others what Jesus had said and done in His earthly life, marvelous words, unheard of miracles, but he had been directly illuminated by God with understanding of those words and miracles. For him the new religion began at Golgotha not at Bethlehem. Not from a cradle of straw, but from an uncovered grave.

This was the God he had heralded in his apostolate among the Gentiles, who found it easier to believe, and among the Jews, too, if they were disposed to believe.

And now, behold! What sorrow! The brethren received him like a malefactor, and the iniquitous word "intruder" reached his ears.

He would have wept. But he raised his head. Frustration

tempered his pride and his will to struggle. He would fulfill to the end the work God had entrusted to him; he would reach the goal God had set him, even at the cost of collapsing at the foot of that goal, as the herald who brought the cry of victory to Marathon had fallen at the foot of the altar. Like a man climbing a mountain, at every step he saw the horizons of the panorama widen, and higher rose the peaks on those horizons. He also saw how the little men fastened to the rock of their Law remained small. But he was sad.

He left Jerusalem like a man who had been there unobserved. Not even his historian Luke speaks of it; in fact, he skips over Paul's brief stay in the Holy City as though he did not know of it. Paul will be told that his fine churches in Galatia, Antioch, Pisidia, Lystra, Derbe, and Iconium are falling to pieces, gnawed by rodents. They were collapsing because the ground was dug away under his feet, but they would rise again. And perhaps never before had he seen so clear and whole and unshakeable as now he saw the great edifice for which he was bringing the foundation stones. Evil reports and enmities only augmented his conviction of being on the right road. Every pagan who had become a Christian was his creature and before many centuries pass the world will be populated with his creatures, infinite harvest from his handful of seed.

The wondrous vision of Christianity triumphant which his ardent words had created for the saints that day at the Council of Jerusalem when he came back from his first journey, his spirit proud and full of youthful Joy, oh, there were those who wanted to erase it from the world! But he saw it always because it had been impressed on his soul by the hand of God.

When he came back to Antioch, he found a little warmth. There was Barnabas who came to meet him as he had the first time. Explanations were not needed for a reconciliation because there had been no disagreement, only Paul's outburst, which he certainly regretted and which the other had forgotten. And there was John Mark. Paul recognized that John Mark was a young man to bear in mind. And he would bear him in mind.

Perhaps Peter, too, was at Antioch in those days. There was Titus. And many of his first converts who had remained loyal to him. But his destiny was to travel. He knew himself to be a man perpetually running toward a prize, toward a vision. The voice of God kept him in perpetual exaltation. "I have set thee for a light to the gentiles, that thou shouldst be for salvation unto the ends of the earth."

And permitting himself no rest, he left for his third mission. Silvanus went back to Peter.

23

The Great Church at Ephesus

After five years he revisited his churches in Galatia which he found in disorder and discord. Other preachers had passed after him and had preached other counsels and precepts. "False brethren had insinuated themselves into the churches to explore the liberties permitted them by Jesus." His word was doubted. They no longer knew how to defend him. He entrusted his churches to those who had remained faithful to him and went forward. He could not stop. He also asked that they collect money for the very poor church of Jerusalem. He would pick it up on his return from his third voyage. He wanted to make a big collection.

Again sadness. His churches were getting out of line. In pain he had brought forth children, and they were ready to deny him. Who watched over the emissaries sent to watch over him? These zealots who impoverished the universal mission of Jesus to a sort of strictly Jewish muster were not really Christians! It was fated that his being far away should separate his churches from him. Forward!

His native pride sprang back from the humiliation. "We are full of tribulations but not oppressed, we are hesitant but not despairing, we are persecuted but not abandoned, beaten but not dead . . . When we are weakest then are we strongest."

He stopped at Ephesus, the last great city of Asia and Greece still to be led by Christ.

He found Aquila and Priscilla there. In a city where the trade in cloth and stuffs was flourishing and money plentiful, they had found the fortune they had vainly sought at Corinth. And in the months he had been away they had prepared the ground for him, and the Christian community of Ephesus was already born. Twelve neophytes had been instructed in the new doctrine, and they were awaiting the last touch from the master before dedicating themselves, too, to the propaganda of the faith.

Aquila and Priscilla had been unexpectedly helped in their work by a highly educated young Alexandrian philosopher. Judaism was already widespread in Egypt and there was a great temple at Leontopolis, almost a counter to the Temple of Jerusalem. This young philosopher came out of the almost Christian school of Philo. He had received confused information about the new spiritual movements developing in Palestine and had had himself baptized after the baptism of John the Baptist. Aquila sought to clarify his ideas and to introduce him to Christ's doctrine as shaped by Paul's concepts.

The young philosopher was called Apollos or Apollonios. A handsome youth, a musical and very graceful orator, master of a perfect Greek tongue, he immediately found an audience which let itself be led by him. He preached some months at Ephesus, then, perhaps spurred and advised by Aquila or perhaps on his own adventurous impulse, he left for Corinth.

Paul did not find him when he reached Ephesus, but he found the fruits of the good work he had accomplished.

He took up that work and perfected it. His eloquence was another thing entirely. Inelegant and meager of person, his words unadorned and almost labored, his severe ideas expressed in quite crude Greek, he succeeded in being highly effective because he was transfigured by the order of his passion. Apollos, the esthete, delighted the refined and cultivated; it was a joy to listen to him: Paul, the polemicist, wrought up and moved the simple souls almost to the point of subjugation. Perhaps for this reason, too, they were tempted to liberate themselves from that yoke when he went away.

Three months he spoke to the Ephesians, outlining his doctrine in the synagogue, then the usual war ensued, and since it was summer he went outside to speak in the open air, along the rivers which almost encircled the city with clear waters and pleasant banks, or along the seashore. When winter returned, he resumed the custom of Philippi, which was to gather a few persons around the hearth of a friendly house and to speak familiarly with them. Sweet repose for his fevered brain, if he could grant himself the sweetness of repose. But the city was large, and he also needed a great auditorium and a pulpit. He went in search of a suitable place and found it in the school offered him by a pedagogue named Tyrannus.

Tyrannus gave lessons in the morning till eleven o'clock. Paul followed from eleven till evening.

The bases of a great church had been laid and it grew rapidly to the point of equaling Jerusalem and Antioch. In the heart of the church a group of responsible superintendents was formed and called the episcopals. A sort of *etat-major* or headquarters gathered around the leader. Many had followed him; others came to join him from Achaia and Macedonia, from Galatia, Phrygia, Pisidia, from Miletus and Smyrna, from Magnesia and Sardis, Thyatira and Pergamos. Men and women. There were Epenetus, one of his first fruits, Urbanus, Apelles, Rufus, Mary and Junias, Triphaena and Triphosa and Persis, Phlegon, Julia, Patrobus, Hermes, Philolocus, Ampliatus, Herodion, Stachys, Asyncritus, Nereus, Olympas, Aristobulus and Narcissus, Hymenis, Philologus, and Hermogene. History opens a spyhole on the obscure crowd of the anonymous and with a fleeting ray of light illumines these names which present themselves. Names not faces.

They came from all over, and he sent them out again. Not being able to be everywhere in person, he sent disciples to bear his word to Phrygia and Lycaonia. Ephesus was not a single church but the center of a vast constellation. Eupaphras, "a man truly apostolic," founded the church of Colossus.

Ephesus was a beautiful city, grandiose, opulent, and full of delights—one of the three holy cities of Greco-Judaic antiquity. The Ionian ease which spread out over the whole coast and the islands had its reservoir in Ephesus. The magnificent landscape extending from the mountain to the sea concentrated enchantment and invitation in the lagoon of the Cayster, where nymphs no longer hid themselves but still swam together with white swans; they were the most beautiful flowering of the Greek line mingled with the Oriental.

Ionic art, which had created divine works in every city, from Pergabos to Sardis, Thyatira to Smyrna, had collected masterpieces by Phidias, Polycletus, Scopas, Praxiteles, Lysippus, Parrhasus, Zeuxis, and Apelles in Ephesus. In Paul's day the temple of Artemis, reconstructed on the ruins of their masterpieces, was not as beautiful, but it was enormous. The Great Theater of Ephesus was famous as the largest in the world; and all of Asia had come together to erect it on its one hundred twenty columns. Mount Cadmus, the colossal mountain behind her, was the Olympus of Asia.

192

The riches accumulated by the Ephesian merchants were fabulous. The sickening luxury of her overfed middle class had no equal. The city's market was an emporium, a caravansery of fortunetellers, sorcerers, clowns, and eunuchs. Born of Greece, Ephesus no longer retained anything of the mother Ephesian but the language and the early monuments. Artemis was an Oriental deity, no longer the Hellenic sister of Apollo, in the cult as in the features of the great black stone statue in the temple chock full of clusters of breasts. A literature of obscene novels bloomed there, the *grammata ephesia*, delectation of ladies and courtesans. Occultists, exorcisers, and theosophers kept school and trade there. Here the astrologer Balbillus was born, who would go to Rome to amuse and educate Nero.

But the responses of the spirit are all the more ready and lively when the action of the material is heavy. The pre-Socratic school of philosophy was born in Ephesus; here Pythagoras may have founded his school of sublime ethical and ascetic questing. Here Heraclitus had devoted himself to the supreme investigation of the logos by means of the secret harmonies and disharmonies of nature. And now it happened that in the midst of the general licentiousness a poor slave would be born in the Ephesian territory who was to be a strong thinker and gentle teacher, the slave philosopher Epictetus, master of virtue. And the neo-Pythagorian Apollonius of Tyana, half magician, half philosopher, would preach his austere morality in the very same period. And the inflammatory words of the Apostle Paul of Tarsus would rouse fires of mystic enthusiasm.

A society must dissolve almost to the point of putrefaction so that it can be born with a new face and new blood, and the new ideas suck the ferments from the steepings of the old ideas. By now Ephesus was a completely denationalized city, which played its part in the rapid and extensive spread of Christianity inside her walls. Internationalism is a soil where religions and madness easily take root. Where the tradition of a great past is on the verge of extinguishment, great revolutions are kindled.

Paul and his disciples had great success with little difficulty. Against his wishes, which were to convert souls not to turn wits, the fame of a thaumaturge, a worker of miraculous healings, spread around his name. From the outlying districts came woodsmen and mountaineers to ask for a token from his person, any little object at all to bring back to their huts for a talisman. They secretly asked Priscilla and the other women who ministered to his needs to let them have something he always wore on his body, a rag or piece of cloth, and took it with them to heal their wounds and sores.

The seven sons of the Jew Sceva, a famous exorciser and chief priest, had devoted themselves to exorcising in the vicinity and claimed to chase evil spirits from the bodies of poor obsessed creatures with the name of Jesus preached by Paul. But one day the people saw the evil spirits refuse to come out, in fact they hurled themselves on the exorcisers and beat them, leaving them lifeless on the ground. Great fear and veneration spread through the city and through all of Asia, for Paul and for the Christ he preached.

Unheard-of events followed. Gentiles and Jews fraternized to be together in Paul's family. They flocked to him to confess themselves and be absolved of every sin. The striving for penitence ran through alleys, markets, and theaters. They lit bonfires in the middle of the city squares, and young and old, men and women, threw into the fire everything they had that was most valuable and impure, the obscene novels, the lewd amulets. They burned thousands and thousands of books, to the value of five thousand denarii, says the historian. A bonfire was made of all the city's bookstores.

But Paul was not happy; he was sad.

194

Came the days of humiliation, of tears and trials. "To this very hour we hunger and thirst and are naked."

And if the news that reached him from the Galatian churches was not such as to rejoice him, the news from Corinth was no better. Apollos, whose well-turned oratory had made his preaching at Corinth such a great personal success, came to meet Paul and to receive illumination on many obscurities in his conception of Christianity. He stayed with Paul and loved him. But he also told him of the doctrinaire dissension and moral taint that was gnawing at the Corinthian church.

In a wondrous vision Paul saw the churches his disciples founded around him burning like the tapers of an immense altar, but then he saw fog descend on those little lights and they paled, while winds were already rising to blow them out.

He thought of setting sail for Corinth; his presence was necessary to control that church. But he did not move. This was the third year he had been preaching at Ephesus, and he always found something to say. A few months had sufficed at Thessalonica and Philippi, but then it had been a question of a few dozen followers, here the curious gathered in crowds. The master's task had no end. It was like the labor, the pain, of Sisyphus.

He would have liked to entrust Apollos himself with the peacemaker's task, but Apollos discreetly avoided it. Then he sent Timothy and Erastus ahead with a letter of his. He recommended the collection for Jerusalem above all. He decided to stay in Ephesus until May, to be present at the great spring festivals, always a good occasion for propaganda.

Then a strange event took place which might have cost him his life but which resolved itself in a merry uproar, and he was able to leave unharmed.

Echoing Jesus' divine words, he had always preached that God is not to be worshipped in temples built of man's hands;

now he added that those are not gods which are made with mortal hands. The daily presence of all the Ephesian marbles and the symbols cluttering up their sacred places was added to the recollection of all the statues and altars he had already seen in Athens. The trade in silver objects and precious stones used in the cult of Artemis was the pride of Ephesus, and now Paul's preaching was taking people away from that cult, and seriously harming the silversmiths and causing unemployment among the artisans.

A certain Demetrius, who had a large silverworking business, brought together his workmen one day and explained how work and profits were dwindling. He named Paul as the author of the crisis, for he was changing people's feelings with his foolish talk. And he cried, "Not only is there danger that this our trade fall into disrepute, but also that the temple of the great goddess Artemis be reckoned of no account and even that something be taken away from the greatness of her whom all Asia and the world doth worship."

The audience was wrought up by the orator's patriotic words. A tumult followed; they went crying through the streets, "Great is Artemis of the Ephesians!" Crowds rushed to the theater where there was room for an enormous meeting, and meanwhile they laid hands on Paul's major disciples, Gaius and Aristarchus. The others protected the master; they kept him at home to prevent him from going to the theater, which was what he wanted to do. Those in charge of theatrical spectacles also sent word begging him not to show himself.

Meanwhile great confusion was taking place at the theater. A Jew named Alexander was taken by the crowd and thrust forward to speak in public. Why he was chosen is not known. Was he a friend? an enemy? a would-be traitor? He made a gesture that he wanted to speak, but what he wanted to say is not clear, nor why the crowd then prevented him from speaking. They continued to shout "Great is Artemis of the Ephesians!" and they exhausted their confusion and their light-hearted revolt with repeated shouting.

When the proconsul's secretary had calmed them enough to speak, he was very clever and persuasive. Who is there who does not know, he said, that Artemis, the daughter of Zeus, is a great goddess and that the city of Ephesus worships her great Artemis? So that there can be no doubt of this, let her good people calm themselves and leave these preachers in peace; they do not rob your church nor blaspheme your goddess. If Demetrius and his artisans have accusations to place against someone, there are the tribunals and the proconsuls, who are well able to award justice. In any event, a legitimate meeting can be arranged, but this is sedition and "we are in danger of being charged with riot in respect to today's assembly. . . ."

The crowd saw reason and dispersed. But it had obtained what it sought. Paul realized that Ephesus was no longer a healthy place for him, and he needed to live a while yet. He left most of his disciples in Asia; they would then rejoin him in small groups. He sent Titus with another letter to the Corinthians, and he followed, making the journey partly by land and partly by sea.

24

Rebukes to the Galatians and the Corinthians

Before leaving Ephesus he had written a letter to the churches of Galatia and a first letter to the Corinthians which has been lost, then a second which is to us the first.

He knew now that his ideas came out more powerfully and clearly in letters than in speech. Paul, the violent, was timorous, and when he spoke, his feeling, so imperious within him, may have become cooler and been smothered as it came out. Now the letters were recognized as more effective, and those who received them recognized it too. If they were not always convinced by the word, they were enthralled by the letters. In addition, the letters had the advantage of remaining while the words vanished once he himself was far away. The letters were his continued presence, so from now on he will write many.

He uncovered a vivid epistolary style, unadorned and sparkling, not orderly but provocative. His passionate ardor burnt the papyrus he wrote on. He could write about himself as he had never been able to speak, confess himself openly, exalt himself and rebuke himself, tell how he was born and how he grew up, how he strayed and had been redeemed, tell his defects, virtues, and merits, his errors and faults, vanities and ambitions with superb humility. Especially when he takes off on a flight, with long insistent galopades of rising adjectives, of questions, affirmations, and invective, his epistolary style captures and commands.

He begins calmly. "I marvel that ye are in such haste to desert him who hath called you to pervert the gospel of Christ . . . For I make known to you, brethren, that the gospel preached by me is no gospel of man, nor did I receive or learn it from man, but by revelation from Jesus Christ."

He told the story of his life, from birth, in fact from the days before birth, because God had already set him apart in his mother's womb and called him through His grace to reveal His Son to man. He confirmed his separation from the Law because the Law "hath been our tutor unto Christ that we may be justified through faith. But now that faith hath come, we are no longer under the tutor. For ye are all through your faith sons of God in Christ Jesus. . . . In him is neither Jew nor Greek, neither slave nor free, neither male nor female; for ye are all one person in Christ Jesus."

Because even after the pact of the Great Council the Judaizers intent on destroying his work imposed the rigors of the Law on every converted person, he reaffirmed his own ideas. "The works of the flesh are manifest, of which are fornication, impurity, uncleanliness, idolatry, witchcraft, enmity, strife, jealousy, wrath, dissensions, factions, parties, envy, drunkenness, reveling, and the like. And to these, I warn against such there is no law."

His prose has caught fire. If the Galatian brethren lend an ear to those who seek to lead them astray, promising them justification by means of the Law and not through obedience to the faith, they delude themselves.

The question of circumcision should have been settled, but it was not, for the intransigents were loath to surrender; and Paul launches his anathema against them. "I Paul tell you that if ye let yourselves be circumcised Christ shall profit you nothing. . . . For in Christ Jesus neither circumcision nor uncircumcision availeth anything . . . I am confident in the Lord that ye will come to think with me; and he that is unsettling you shall bear the penalty . . . Would that those who are causing confusion among you would go on to mutilate themselves."

He sorrowfully recalls the joyful days of his first journey to Galatia when he faced so many dangers, persecutions and bodily ills, but was comforted by the tenderness of the first neophytes born from his preaching. "Ye received me as an angel of God as Christ Jesus. Where then is your self-congratulation? Yea, I bear you witness that, if it had been possible, ye had plucked out your eyes and given them to me. Am I, then, become your enemy, because I tell you the truth? They are courting you from no good motive, nay, they wish to shut you out, that ye may court them. Yet it is good to be courted for a good motive at all times, and not only when I am with you, my children, with whom I am again in travail, until Christ be formed in you."

After the first lost letter, he wrote a second letter to the Corinthians and sent it with Titus. This too was a letter of rebuke and self-justification. The Corinthians had also written to him and had sent the letter with three of the church leaders, Stephanas, Fortunatus, and Achaius, to give him news about the theological lurches which were threatening to dissolve their church, despite its wealth and numbers. Paul did not keep that letter, he never kept them, and we can understand how many letters were written to him from all over. Revolutionaries who go where the wind bears them and have no house in which to rest cannot conserve the letters they receive, and it is fortunate for history that others conserve those they write. (Mazzini, who seeded Europe with his own letters, did not keep a single one of the hundred thousand his comrades in faith wrote to him.)

Involuntary cause of the Corinthian controversy had been Apollos, in particular, with his spiritual eschatology of Philonian stamp. Perhaps this was why the honest rival had left Corinth to meet Paul at Ephesus, not wanting to aggravate the situation, and now did not want to return. There was also a faction for Peter in the process of formation at Corinth. This news certainly afflicted the apostle, but he may have been more disturbed by the scandals come to contaminate his church, such as an incestuous brother who flaunted his sin in public. Paul replied to the one and the other in the letter sent with Titus.

It is a long letter. He doesn't need to fight much against the fomenters discord, and a few blows, glancing at first, then full force, are enough to dispose of them. "For when one saith, 'I am for Paul,' and another, 'I am for Apollos,' are ye not simply men? What then is Apollos? What is Paul? Ministers through whom ye believed, even as to each the Lord gave power. I planted, Apollos watered, but God the while was making to grow. So then neither he that planteth is anything nor he that watereth, but God who maketh to grow. And he that planteth and he that watereth are but one, yet shall each receive his own reward according to his own toil. For we are God's fellow workers, and ye are God's tillage, God's building.

According to the grace of God bestowed on me, like a skillful master-builder I laid the foundation, and now another is building thereon. Let each look to it how he buildeth. Foundation can no man lay other than that which is already laid, which is Jesus Christ."

Because he was already preparing to go himself to Corinth, he would say the rest personally, with persuasive words. But writing, he would not contain an explosion of cutting sarcasm and irony. "We are become a spectacle to the world, both to angels and men. We are fools for Christ, but ye are wise in Christ: we are weak, but ye are strong: ye have glory, but we dishonor. To this very hour we hunger and thirst and are naked and are buffeted, we are homeless and we toil, working with our own hands. We are reviled and we bless, we are persecuted and we endure, we are defamed and we answer softly; we have become as refuse of the world, the offscouring of all men, even to this hour!"

He had especially explained his dogma to the Galatians, whose thoughts had been led astray by the Judaizers. He gives a moral sermon to the Corinthians, corrupted in their emotions and ways of living. Preoccupation with morals is always present in his thought. After having consigned the incestuous man to Satan, he severely rebukes all those guilty of kindred errors, "neither fornicators, nor idolators nor adulterers nor effeminates, nor sodomites nor thieves nor cheats, nor drunkards, nor railers, nor robbers shall inherit the kingdom of God." Then he clarifies his ideas on the subject of matrimony, not disapproving of it, though he really considers celibacy the better condition for the perfect liberty of spirit, but it is better to marry than to burn.

Above all he is anxious to dissipate many misunderstandings which have risen from his kind ways with women, to the point of receiving them even in the liturgy of the church. There were women who mistook that courtesy for weakness, almost for cajolery, so that the Sunday Eucharist degenerated into banquets ending in dancing and drunkenness. He recalled them, and the men with them, to sober and honest living. "Have ye not homes in which to eat and drink? Or do you despise the church of God and put to shame the needy? . . . If anyone is hungry, let him eat at home, lest ye meet together only for judgment. The rest I shall set in order when I come." So from admonition to admonition, from counsel to counsel, his tone rises until he sings the hymn of love, peak of all virtues. "If I speak with the tongues of men and of angels, but have not charity, I am become as sounding brass or a clanging cymbal. And if I have the gift of prophecy, and comprehend all mysteries and all knowledge; and if I have all faith, so as to displace mountains, and have not charity, I am nothing. And if I bestow in doles all my goods, and if I deliver my body to the flames, but have not charity, it profiteth nothing. Charity is patient, is kind; charity envieth not, is not pretentious, is not puffed up, behaveth not amiss, seeketh not her own, is not provoked, regardeth not evil; rejoiceth not over wickedness, but rejoiceth with the truth; beareth all things, believeth all things, hopeth all things, endureth all things."

He remained at Ephesus and awaited Titus' return impatiently. He was anxious to hear how the Corinthians had taken his outburst. He feared he had gone too far. He would not want the women to take offense. But after the disturbance roused by the silversmith Demetrius, the brethren advised him to depart, and he left before Titus came back. He went toward his disciple on the land route and found him along the road.

He had promised he would arrive at Corinth by a certain date: since he had to take a long way round he could not be there on that date, and the worried Corinthians would reproach him for that delay, they would accuse him of fickleness, but it was not his fault. To meet Titus, he had to go by way of Asia, through Thrace, Macedonia, and Thessaly, and still he did not find him. He waited for him at Troas, where, in the meantime, he founded another church. Finally he reached him at Philippi. But Titus had good news, and after so much difficulty, so much pain and palpitation (he is not a happy man; he cannot be, never will be except in prayer and the expectation of God), Paul at least draws a breath of relief.

His Corinthians have not abandoned him: they have remained faithful to him, they obey him, they follow him, they love him. He is calmed, and he does not immediately resume his journey. He decides to inspect the churches of Macedonia and writes them a second letter.

Trying to be more gentle, he succeeds a little bit. He wants to erase the impression of severity his first letter had left. He begins by dictating humble and subdued words to his secretary. But bit by bit those quiet words raise their pitch and begin to resound. It would not be Paul if after the first quiet chords he did not burst out sonorously with all the horns in the symphony of pride. The sweep of language swells to a tempest. He speaks of himself, asks pardon for doing so, and speaks of himself again. Again he asks pardon, and more loudly he goes back.

He says he does not lose heart, for "though our outer man is decaying, yet is our inner man being renewed day by day." He is most haughty in the consciousness of his apostleship when he is at his most humble and modest. He knows he will not be able to say these things aloud to his young faithful, to his dear deaconesses; he will not want to say harsh words to them but only loving ones.

"But in everything we commend ourselves as the ministers of God, in much patience; in tribulations, in hardships, in straits; in stripes, in imprisonments, in tumults; in labors, in watchings, in fastings; in chastity, in knowledge, in longsuffering, in goodness, in the Holy Spirit, in charity unfeigned, in the word of truth, in the power of God; with the armor of justness on the right hand and on the left, in glory and dishonor, in evil report and in good report, as deceivers and yet truthful, as unknown and yet well known, as 'dying and behold we live, as chastised and yet not done to death,' as mourning yet ever rejoicing, as poor yet enriching many, as having naught yet possessing all things."

"For I esteem myself in no way to have fallen short of the most eminent apostles. For though perchance unskilled in speech, yet am I not in knowledge." Then, "By the truth of Christ which is in me, this same boast shall not be debarred to me in the districts of Achaia!"

And again, "They are Hebrews? So am I! They are Israelites? So am I! They are ministers of Christ? I—I speak as one beside himself—I am more: in labors more abundantly, in prisons more abundantly, in stripes above measure, in deaths often. From the Jews five times did I receive forty stripes save one, thrice was I beaten with rods, once was I stoned, thrice was I shipwrecked, a night and a day have I passed in the depths of the sea: in journeyings often, in perils from rivers, perils from robbers, perils from mine own nation, perils from the heathen, perils in city, perils in wilderness, perils in the sea, perils from false brethren: in labor and toil, in watchings often, in hunger and thirst, in fastings often, in cold and nakedness. . . ."

And finally, bitter sarcasm: "In what, pray, were ye put to a disadvantage compared to the rest of the churches—unless it were that I myself was not a burden to you? Pardon me this injustice!"

He also enjoins them to collect much money to send to Jerusalem, to vie with each to see who can collect most, eagerly and joyously. ("Give without regret; God wants you to give with happiness.") The question of the collection becomes a dominating idea with him. From a work of generosity, helping the poor at Jerusalem, he elevates it to a principle of solidarity and universal equality. "Your abundance did not lack."

Only when he can be sure that there has been an abundant collection of money, that the souls in the church have been pacified and the unworthy thrown out, does he leave for Corinth. And many disciples follow him.

At Corinth he wanted above all to take care of himself because he was sick, to rest because he was tired; to be left in calm because he had another letter to write. Now he knew that he could not reach Rome this time either, because he had been four years journeying and he must bring to Jerusalem the large sums of money collected. His friend Gaius received him at his house, where, except to fulfill his duties in the Sunday Eucharist, the agape, he kept himself cloistered to meditate and to dictate a long letter to his secretary Timothy. Since he cannot have the Romans as listeners, he is sending them this letter.

From the first day he made it a principle not to work in the field of others, and for this reason, too, he was of two minds about embarking for Italy. But he can tell his idea to the Romans, even if they are not his children. The letter he now writes is not only for them. He will send it to all the churches, in addition to Rome. Because old age approaches, and the dangers grow with his enemies, while his strength dwindles, he wants to leave a definitive testament of his theology. After all, if the others invade his field and upset everything, it is foolish not to repay them in the same coin; he who is apostle as much as the greatest, in fact with more right.

The secretaries made several copies of the letter and he entrusted it to the missionaries for circulation. The deaconess Phoebe, of the little church of Cenchrea, brings it to Rome.

25

"It Is More Blessed to Give Than to Receive"

The letter to the Romans, the most ample together with the first to the Corinthians, contains a summary of Paul's entire doctrine, which was scattered and somewhat fragmented by the polemic agitation of the preceding letters. Not having a well-defined adversary to fight, his language is less roused by passion and rises to greater serenity, and within the peaceable words his thoughts are reflected with sharper outlines. There is room in these pages for only a quick glance, because the scope of this book is only the narration of certain extraordinary lives in an extraordinary, almost supernatural time.

The foundation of Paul's doctrine is the justification of divine grace in virtue and not in the acts prescribed by the Law. Divested of the dross of dialectic turnings, of irony and

209

sarcasm, this letter, liberated from the Law contains not a way to salvation but only a norm of education and, therefore, is of only transitory power and more naked and more solid, for to know this doctrine in all its parts one must read the entire letter. It is an offense to Jesus, he concludes finally, to believe that salvation can be obtained with the simple observance of the Law, without faith in Jesus, without the grace of Jesus.

In the preceding letters the apostle has rid himself of every remnant of bitterness that disappointments and humiliation had deposited in his heart. He has given vent to his rage against the destroyers of his work, against the perturbers of consciences whom he had educated to the faith. There is no further need to put his own merits and virtues forward, what he has done and what he has suffered, because self-justification is really renewed humiliation to one who must look to it to defend himself against lies and calumny.

If he goes back to confess the sins of his youth, which he has touched on at other times, he insists on them to demonstrate the inefficiency of the Law, and more, its evil properties when followed without discernment. "Is the Law sin? Heaven forbid! Yet I knew not sin save through the Law. For indeed I had not known lust, if the Law had not said, 'Thou shalt not lust'; but sin, getting a hold on me through the commandment, worked all manner of lust in me; for without the Law sin is dead. I was once living without the Law; but when the commandments came sin sprang into life, and I died, and the very commandment that was for life, I found to be my death. For sin, getting a hold on me through the commandment, deceived me and killed me thereby. . . . Unhappy man that I am! Who will deliver me from the body of this death? Thanks be to God through our Lord Jesus Christ."

From his own personal instance he rises to expand upon the universe. The confession unfolds before the reader's eyes the historic panorama of humankind in an analogy with his own life, sinner until Jesus, after Jesus redeemed. The Pauline doctrine of original sin is defined and completed in this letter.

When the letter was sent and the collection money gathered, he decided to return by the shortest route to Jerusalem, by sea, and he hired a vessel in the port of Cenchrea for himself and the disciples of his train, by now about twenty. He had always gone in a small group of one or two youths, but now from all over the best gathered round him, bringing him the collections from faraway churches. Physically he no longer had the health or strength of former times; his old illness pricked him more painfully. Also the plots of his adversaries were growing, and consequently his younger and stronger disciples stayed close around him.

In fact word arrived of a plot that was being woven against him, perhaps the revenge of the incestuous brother consigned to Satan. Instead of venturing out to the high seas, he accepted the suggestion to hug the coast, following the great arc of the Aegean shore. He had planned to be in Jerusalem at Easter and to present his gift to the great church on that holy day, but by Easter he had only just reached Philippi, and he stopped there to celebrate the holiday. At Philippi, Luke, the doctor and historian, returned to the company.

From Philippi they went on to Troas. Paul sent the ship ahead, and he and Luke rejoined the others by land. The reason for this arduous and secret journey is not known: perhaps small churches were scattered along the mountain road. At

Troas they stopped for a week. Here a miraculous event took place. Paul spoke one evening after the agape in a friend's house. He spoke at length. The little church at Troas had grown. The seedlings set out only a few months before had been watered by an unknown Apollos. Paul spoke at length because he always had a great deal to say. It was the eve of his departure, and he did not know whether he would return. At midnight he was still speaking.

Then it was that the miraculous happening occurred. A boy was listening to him seated astride a windowsill, to cool off on the muggy night. He was overpowered by sleep and fell from the third-story height. They ran to pick up the lifeless body and no one had any hope of saving him, but Paul encouraged his family and friends with words of hope and brought the boy back to life. Calmly he continued to speak until dawn, then as soon as the sky lightened, the apostle's group left.

This time, too, he sent the others to Assos by boat and he followed them on foot, cutting across the peninsula. At Assos they all boarded ship, threaded through the canal of Chios and touched shore the next day at the island of Samos, the third day at Miletus. They had sailed in sight of Ephesus without landing. Ephesus was not a city to stay in for only a few days. Paul, who knew his men and himself, realized it would have been difficult to leave Ephesus, and with Easter already past, he would not even arrive at Jerusalem for Pentecost.

He wanted to see the leaders of the Ephesian church, however, and he called them to Miletus. He made a long speech to them, in contrast to his always ardent spirit, a pathetic and melancholy discourse, almost a last farewell. One is surprised to hear the sweet echo of Jesus, Son of Man, in the apostle's words. Perhaps Paul had learned many of the Master's words before His death and resurrection from new people encountered about this time or from Luke, who had heard them from the Mother's voice and from the last survivors.

He told his twelve Ephesian episcopals that bonds and afflictions awaited him at Jerusalem, just as Jesus had said to his twelve apostles that he was making his way toward the holy city which kills its prophets.

Paul said, "And now, behold, I know that ye shall see my face no longer, all ye among whom I went about preaching the kingdom."

"I know that after my departure grievous wolves shall come in among you, not sparing the flock; and from among your own selves shall arise men speaking perverse things. . . ."

After recalling once again his poor and modest life, that he had never been a weight on anyone, he said that he had learned from the Master the precept that "It is more blessed to give than to receive." None of the four chroniclers of the Gospels repeats these words of Jesus. Paul had plucked them from the air.

From Miletus they weighed anchor for Cos, from Cos for Rhodes, from Rhodes for Patara on the mainland. In Lycian Patara they boarded a new vessel and, crossing the Mediterranean south of Cyprus, they landed at Tyre in Phoenicia, where the ship unloaded its cargo.

There were many disciples waiting the apostle at Tyre, and they stayed there seven days. The disciples had been moved by sad presentiments and had come to try to dissuade Paul from proceeding on his voyage to Jerusalem, but it was like telling the general to withdraw to his tent in the moment that he gives the command for battle. Paul continued, and those disciples and their wives and sons went with him all the way to the shore, prostrating themselves at his feet and embracing his knees.

From Tyre to Ptolemais for a brief stopover, then to Caesarea. Here the insistence that he should not go to Jerusalem was more pressing and mysterious. The evangelist Philip and his four prophetess daughters received the missionaries. They stayed there several more days, and before they could leave the prophet Agabus, bearer of fears and disasters, came to join them. This terrible man accompanied his catastrophic predictions with a sorcerer's gestures, and he seized Paul's belt and bound his hands and feet with it, crying: "Thus saith the Holy Spirit: so shall the Jews bind at Jerusalem the man whose is this girdle, and they shall deliver him into the hands of the gentiles."

Horror struck the disciples who supplicated Paul not to leave Caesarea, but Paul spoke to them as Jesus would have, saying: "What are ye doing thus weeping and breaking my heart? I am not only ready to be bound, but to die at Jerusalem for the name of the Lord Jesus."

To which the other could only answer, "The Lord's will be done." And they followed him to Jerusalem.

A disciple named Mnason of Cyprus, who had a great house at Jerusalem, went with them, and he gave them shelter in his house.

At Jerusalem they found cordial welcome among the leaders but ill-concealed hostility on the margins of the community. But the open-hearted and serene Peter was not there. Not even John was there since the death of the Mother, who had been entrusted to his care, and consoled and supported by

him. He too had left on a mission to Asia in the Ephesian territory. His preaching was not less ardent and vehement than that
of Paul, but different, rather more faithful to the Law and less
revolutionary. Only one of the pillars remained in the Mother
Church, James.

26

"When I Am Weak,
Then Am I Strong"

Had the apostle become the apostate? The compromise of fifteen years earlier no longer had any value because, in the meantime, new people had been admitted to the Christian community and, as happens in every association, the newcomers, young, audacious, and intractable, had taken the lead over the old leaders. This was the fourth time since Damascus that Paul came to Jerusalem, and each time he found something that stopped him at the border, rejecting him with an ever more hostile voice: "you are an outsider!"

It is in the logic of human hurts and feelings that Paul's authority and independent spirit, now arrived at such a height, should offend the Pharisees who were now in power over the conciliatory party in Jerusalem. That height cast too big a shadow. He had immeasurably broadened the field of action assigned him by the Great Council, and certainly no one had then imagined that he would have brought such a worrisome crowd of pagans into that field. He said he did not want to sow in others' soil, but in truth, feeling himself a better sower than they; he leaped all hedges. Finally, and on this especially the intransigents insisted, let him do what he pleased with his pagans, but the Jews, even though baptized Christians, must remain Jews in the Law.

Truly the last four years had worked away heavily against him. He felt himself excluded and rejected by the young people, whom he particularly wanted to approach. If not for Mnason, he might not have found roof or bed. Was the conqueror of souls a penitent, a postulant?

The collections, too, were ill received by these suspicious people. They feared Paul even in the act of offering gifts. His gift was infinitely greater than a poorbox. He brought a new religious and moral world to Jerusalem: fourteen centuries later a similar reception would be given to one who brought a new earthly world as a gift to his king.

He had ordered many young people to go with him, each one bearing the well-sealed offering of his church, not wanting to take all the credit for those large sums himself. (He understood human nature.) But that money which he wanted only out of generosity to the city's poor was taken by his illwishers as an ostentation of alms-giving, almost as the tangible evidence of Paul's success and authority. They wanted to humiliate the lofty one. The nabob, he was sneering at their holy poverty! And Paul was so candid, or so proud, that to that tangible sign of his power he added a speech telling everything he had accomplished. It was the weakness of a strong man, doubly exasperating to the truly weak.

They had to force humiliation—put his Jewishness to public test and make him bend his haughty head.

They found four men who had taken the Nazirite vow, which entailed a certain expense in the execution of the rite and the offering of the votive animals to God. Often poor people were not able to undertake this expense and the money was offered for them by richer Jews.

"These four are poor," the fanatics said to Paul, "take them with you; be sanctified with them, and you pay for them. All who have listened to you will know that you still observe the Law, and that what has been said of you is not true; it is not the words but the acts that signify."

As to the Gentiles he was converting, no secret was kept that they had taken steps to send letters and preachers out to put them back on the right road. Paul knew it.

Humiliate himself, then? They wanted a public act of contrition from him who had not sinned. They did not pardon him for being what he was, for doing what he had done, what only he could have done. Bow to the Law then? Perform all that which was most uselessly figurative and ceremonial in the Law? Put himself in a self-contradictory position? He had undertaken that rite for himself four years before: why force him to perform it for others too?

To avoid scandals, which would have hurt the church not the man, he would bend his head all the same, renounce his liberty of spirit. There came back to his memory the words already written to the Galatians, the Corinthians, the Romans, the words he had said so many times: "I made myself a Jew with the Jews. . . . Being free of all I made myself a slave. . . ." And he again made himself a Jew, made himself a slave again. It was his greatest sacrifice.

But it was not enough. Safely out of the hands of the Jewish Christians, he fell into those of the Jews themselves. Considered overzealous by the leaders of his religion, for the Jewish zealots he was always a renegade. Certain of them who had undoubtedly been following him for days saw him in the temple and seized hold of him. They dragged him outside, crying that he defiled the temple, and a great crowd was attracted. They recognized him; it was the renegade, their bitterest enemy, the man who went about the whole world preaching against the Law of Moses, the perverter of the people. They had seen him at Ephesus, and were still burning from the recent memory. They accused him of the severe crime of profanation of the temple by bringing in a pagan, the Ephesian Trophimus. A foolish accusation because, though Paul had certainly walked on the city streets in Trophimus' company, he was not so foolhardy as to take him into the temple, beyond the Court of the Gentiles. He knew well what was carved on the innermost wall of that court: "pain of death" for a Gentile who ventured further.

They had dragged him outside to kill him immediately in an unsanctified spot. They barred the temple doors so he would not try to re-enter. And they would have killed him if the tribune of the Roman cohort had not intervened in time. Centurions and soldiers arrived; the furious crowd relaxed its hold. Resolutely, the tribune made them give up Paul. He asked who they were and what they wanted of him, but unable to make anything out of the deafening hubbub, they ordered him brought into the fortress Antonia while those behind shouted, "Kill him! Kill him!"

On the steps of the fort, free of the riot, Paul asked the tribune if he could speak to him. He spoke in the tongue of the centurion.

"You know Greek, then?" the tribune said.

He was under a misapprehension. They had told him of an Egyptian Jew, a sorcerer who passed himself off as God's envoy, Who shortly before had assembled four thousand, or thirty thousand, followers and marched against Jerusalem. Camped on the Mount of Olives, this Egyptian had proclaimed that with one word he would bring down the city walls. He and his followers were wiped out by the Roman soldiers. Lysias, the tribune, thought that the charlatan had fled while his followers were dying and had now come back to the city to renew his insane attempts. And he thought that Paul was this man.

Paul replied, "Certainly, I am a Jew, a citizen of Tarsus in Cilicia, a city not unknown, but I am not the One you think. I beg you, permit me to speak to the people."

The permission given, Paul made a long speech in Aramaic to the people, telling of his past errors and of his redemption by Jesus' appearance, and of the beginning of his mission. It was not the first time he had spoken thus; the self-apology was a part of his preaching, but he now added a note of challenge. The people would not allow him to continue: there were screams and yells, people tore off his clothes and threw stones. At last, the tribune, unable to understand further, but terrified by the swelling of the tumult, ordered that the prisoner be taken away and scourged.

Paul asked the centurion who was preparing for the task whether it was legal to scourge an uncondemned Roman citizen. Paul well knew that it was not, and the centurion suspended the execution of his orders to tell his superior about it. Lysias was upset; his death was the punishment for violating this Roman law. But he was unconvinced.

"Roman," he asked the prisoner. "You?"

"Roman," Paul replied.

"I paid dearly for my Roman citizenship," the tribune said.

"But I was born a Roman," said Paul.

Lysias returned to his rooms after ordering them to loose the prisoner's chains, and he decided to present Paul before the synod, which was to meet the following day.

The next day Paul made a very clever and disarming speech to the synod; in fact, it put the priests at odds among themselves.

Proclaiming himself a Pharisee and the son of Pharisees, he said he believed in the resurrection of the flesh, thus setting Pharisees against Sadducees, for the first believed in resurrection and the second denied it. The squabble could have ended badly for him, because, after all, in disagreement among themselves on questions of dogma, they were agreed and most decided on suppression of the perpetual public danger that Paul represented. But the tribune took a hand in it and removed him from the disorder to shut him up again in the fortress while waiting for better advice.

That night something happened which saved Paul from the enraged Jews, at least for the moment. The apostle's sister may still have lived in Jerusalem; what is certain is that a son of hers still lived there. A last ray of family love reappears in the life story of the great prodigal son. The man who denied his family for his mission—exemplary incarnation of Jesus' teaching—cursed and disowned by his father in consequence, now found a sorrowful smile of family feeling as he went toward the evening of his life. The deserter was still the brother. Perhaps the sister had even kept some of the paternal heritage for him. Perhaps the nephew brought him money too.

What he did bring was word of a fanatical plot; forty extremists had united and sworn a solemn vow to kill Paul; they were to fast until the vow was fulfilled. Therefore, they had requested the synod to bring the evildoer before an assembly, ostensibly to continue the inquest, but actually so that they could murder him. At the bottom of their religious hatred of Paul was the fear that he would get them into trouble with Rome—a fear which made them lose their wits.

The boy asked to see his uncle, and permission was granted. What was Paul feeling in this hour of anguish and hope? A man can desert mother, father, wife and sisters, and affections and possessions to go with Jesus and make himself worthy of

Him, but at the end does he not find the face of Jesus in a familiar young face too?

Paul begged the centurion to take the boy to the tribune. Lysias believed him when he spoke, and he had already grasped Paul's sincerity and his moral stature. He told the boy not to say a word to anyone and that he would save his uncle. That very night he ordered two centurions to have two hundred foot soldiers and seventy horsemen ready at three o'clock to escort Paul to Caesarea and bring him to the governor, Felix. He wrote to his superior that the synod had accused Paul on questions of their law, though he had committed no crime deserving of chains or capital punishment. Therefore, he was sending Paul to him so that Felix, governor of Palestine, could settle the controversy.

That night two hundred soldiers escorted Paul as far as Antipatris. The seventy lance-armed horsemen stayed with him until he reached Caesarea. So many things had happened in one week or less.

Paul had had a vision that night before he was awakened. Jesus had appeared to him in a dream and encouraged him, "Be of good cheer, Paul, for as you have testified of me in Jerusalem, so must you bear witness also at Rome."

To Rome, then! He must go to Rome!

27

To Rome, To Rome!

But he was not to go to Rome immediately. For two more years he would remain a prisoner in Palestine.

The governor Felix did not treat him badly, but he did not realize that he must treat him well. He was kind with him; he was not just. A man of mediocre intelligence and besoiled spirit, he committed no serious fault against Paul, however, save that of not liberating him as he undoubtedly deserved. Powerful in Rome because his brother was that Pallas who was a favorite first of Claudius and then of Nero, in Jerusalem (according to Tacitus) he exercised a sovereign's rights in slavish spirit. He could consider himself almost a sovereign for he had married three queens, one after another, and the first was a Jewess, daughter of Herod Agrippa, who had abandoned her husband, the King of Emesa, to marry the uncircumcised Felix. With his servile and sensual soul, he hoped to get money out of Paul, having heard of the generous collections Paul had brought to Rome and perhaps of the money his wealthy sister may have sent him in prison. When he did not succeed, he was infuriated.

He did not immediately throw him into the common criminal's jail; he kept him in custody of Herod's praetorium, waiting until the accusers came from Jerusalem to judge him. The high priest Ananias came, together with the elders and an orator named Tertullus, who had been designated to plead the accusation before the procurator. It was the same accusation of rebellion and profanation of the temple, with the addition of a more picturesque adjective than had yet been applied to Paul. They called him pestiferous. Pestiferous because they feared he was a fomenter of disturbances against Rome, and they thought the adjective would please the Romans.

When Paul had the floor, he defended himself calmly, with the serenity of a man whose conscience is clear. He had never stirred up the people nor profaned the Temple, but had only been preaching the doctrine of Jesus for many years and had even brought money to Jerusalem. Felix had heard of the new religion which was spreading through the world from Judea, but he was not interested in hearing more; he sent the priests away and called the tribune Lysias to tell what he knew. Meanwhile, he took off the prisoner's chains; he even allowed him to receive his comrades. It was then that there flashed on him the hope of extracting money from Paul.

But the money did not come. Instead Paul had a brilliant idea which worsened his condition. The Jewish wife of Felix, Drusilla, was rather more curious than her husband to hear some of the secrets of the new religion preached by the untamable vagabond. She asked her husband to invite him to speak. And Paul spoke. But he changed his tune. Before that so beautiful divorced woman the apostle put dogma aside and made a moral speech; he spoke of justice, of chastity, and of the punishment awaiting the unjust and lascivious. "Stop!" The governor cut him short, and he threw him back into prison and forgot about him. But his was not a malicious vengeance.

Felix was recalled to Rome; he was succeeded by Porcius Festus, a just and honest magistrate who now occupied the seat of the gangster, accomplice, and hireling of more powerful gangsters.

But Felix had not thought of freeing the uncondemned prisoner before he left Caesarea, which was almost a way of abandoning him to the Jews, so that Festus found himself with this ungrateful charge on his hands. As soon as he arrived he visited Jerusalem, as protocol required, and there the priests asked him to turn the prisoner over to them to be judged by the synod. Festus replied that they must come to Caesarea.

The usual accusations were repeated in the new trial, with the addition of a shifty hint at a crime of *lese majesty*. Paul repeated his defense, adding that he had never sinned, not even against Caesar.

The new governor did not doubt Paul's innocence; in any event he was judge only of the last charge, for the others, of purely religious and political nature, he would escort Paul to Jerusalem if he consented to go before the synod to reply to the charges. It was a diplomatic way of granting something to the Jews without removing Paul's protection.

Paul replied simply, "I take my stand before Caesar's tribunal, and I have the right to be tried by Caesar. I have done no wrong to the Jews. If I have done something worthy of death, I do not refuse to die. If I have not committed the crime of which they accuse me, no one can turn me over to them. I appeal to Caesar."

He had drawn his destiny with this reply. Not the synod and not even the governor now had the right to try him. Every Roman citizen who requested it had the right to be tried at Rome by the Emperor.

For Paul it was also the only way—the last hope of reaching Rome.

In those days King Agrippa the Second and his sister, Bernice, passed through Caesarea on a visit to Festus. His sister by birth, but now the widow of the dead King Herod; something else, too, according to the malicious. Sister also of Drusilla and equally beautiful, she was perhaps the most famous beauty of the century, a beauty which sowed scandal and indecent minglings. Star of the first magnitude, no other woman after Cleopatra passed through the Roman and Oriental world in such a blaze of lascivious glory. In ten years' time, as a setting star, she was also to bewitch the Emperor's son, Titus.

Festus had occasion to speak to his guests of the prisoner, the strange, proud being who proclaimed himself apostle of a new religion, of the religion of one Jesus Who was said to be dead and Whom he asserted to be eternally alive. He mentioned the religious accusations laid against him by the priests and the appeal he had addressed to Caesar. Naturally Agrippa, too, grew curious to hear the proud apostle; he asked Festus to let him see Paul, and Festus was grateful to the king for his wish, which offered Festus the occasion to convene the city notables and declare publicly that he found no guilt in the accused nor did he know what accusation to make against him to the Emperor. It seemed unreasonable to him to send a man in chains to Rome without having charges to allege against him; he asked Agrippa to examine the prisoner himself and to dictate something he could write.

Paul made another impetuous speech in Agrippa's presence. Again, he told of his double life, as persecutor of Christians first, and then as apostle. Such was the ardor of his eloquence that Festus thought the orator was taking leave of his senses when he reached the climax of his speech, Christ's ordeal on the Cross and his Resurrection. "You are mad!" he cried. "Your great learning makes you rave."

"I'm not mad, excellent Festus; I say words of sober truth,"

228

Paul replied then, turning to Agrippa, "The king knows these things and I speak freely before him. None of the things I have said are unknown to him, I believe, because I have never done anything secretly. Do you believe in the prophets, O king?"

Not knowing how to reply, Agrippa turned it into a joke, "Now you would like to make me, too, into a Christian."

And he dismissed the assembly to say more seriously to the procurator Festus that he saw no guilt whatsoever in Paul and if he had not already appealed to the Emperor he would have freed him.

The historian Flavius Josephus was also in Caesarea at that time.

They were sending him to Rome! He was going to achieve his life's goal. Finally! This was the autumn of the sixtieth year after Christ's birth. Paul was a little more than fifty years old. The last two years had been lost, inactive ones. Old age had overtaken him before he had completed his youth. His spirit was still vigorous and ready for the struggle but in an organism already so much tried his physical resistance to effort and strains was not what it had been.

The illness that troubled him most, however, was the fear and anxiety for the churches he had founded, for his children scattered in a world full of snares. And his parting words to the brethren are most touching: "The others are your brothers; I am your father. I have given birth to you. . . . But you don't love me as I love you. . . ."

What would become of the many thousands of faithful, not all of whom were yet fortified in the faith and hence might be susceptible to other flattering or threatening voices. He was leaving the field open to his adversaries, who only awaited his departure to invade and devastate it. But he had to go: God would take care of his children. He entrusted the heritage

229

to the most dependable of his disciples and took only three with him, Timothy, Aristarchus, and Luke.

A prison ship was to sail from Caesarea at that time under the command of a centurion of the Augustan cohort, one Julius. The Roman procurator placed Paul and his companions aboard, and the ship weighed anchor and sailed along the Asian coast. The next day they landed at Sidon in Phoenicia and the centurion, a very understanding person (the third good centurion in Christian history), permitted Paul to go freely through the city and to meet with friends and disciples of that city. From Sidon they crossed the seas of Cilicia and Pamphylia and continued toward Myra in Lycia where the ship's journey ended. There they found an Alexandrian ship loaded with wheat that was setting sail for Italy, and the centurion transferred his human freight to this vessel.

A small voice would like to inform us that at Myra, Thecla, the virgin consecrated to God, came to find Paul, to greet him after fifteen years. Why not heed that quiet voice?

28

Awaiting the Trial

It was an adventurous voyage which lasted all through the period of storm and fog, from September till spring. They stopped at Cnidus near Crete because of contrary winds and skirted the southern part of the island to weigh anchor in the roadstead of Fair Havens. Paul, who had some knowledge of navigation, told the centurion that it would be a good idea to spend the winter here, but the centurion entrusted himself to the pilot's advice rather than the prisoner's. He ordered the ship to proceed to the safer harbor of Phenice, which was on the island itself. But storms overtook them, and the ship was blown off course toward the Syrtis. They threw the cargo of grain into the water; they threw rigging and gears overboard; there remained only the excess cargo of men and the prisoners. Battered by the storm for several days, they were short of food with no hope of being saved. But Paul intervened to encourage crew and prisoners. He had had a new vision during the night, a celestial voice had repeated what had already been said at Caesarea. "Fear not, Paul, thou must stand before Caesar."

But when they had been driven across the Adriatic for fourteen days, the crew decided they must be close to land and lowered the shallop to save themselves, leaving the prisoners in God's hands. But Paul spoke again to warn and hearten the crew and the Roman soldiers. He was unassailable in his certainty of reaching Rome safely, and he communicated his certainty to his comrades in pain and peril. They would all be saved with him. Meanwhile, he exhorted them to take food and to trust in Providence.

They ate the hard bread of sailors. At dawn they perceived a bay where they proposed to beach the ship. But it was carried to a sandy spit which was open to the seas, and here it grounded. It was a shipwreck, not a landing, and the ship was fast breaking-up. There was a chance for the prisoners to escape both storm and prison by swimming for shore so the soldiers decided to kill them before they could get away. But the centurion Julius wanted to bring his charge before the Emperor, and he dissuaded them from this useless cruelty.

They were all saved; those who could swam to shore, the others reached the land on planks from the ship. They discovered that the island on which they had been wrecked was called Malta. The natives received the castaways with the concern and kindliness of a seafaring people. They warmed them at their fires and fed them with their own bread. The governor of the island, Publius, entertained the important members of the party at his own home and kept them there three days. It happened that his father was ill of dysentery, and Paul cured him. His fame as a healer spread throughout the island, and all its sick came to the noted prisoner to be made well again. Thus they spent the three winter months on Malta.

They left aboard an Alexandrian ship, stayed three days at Syracuse, one at Reggio, and with favorable winds blowing reached Pozzuoli in another two days, in Italy at last.

They had crossed the sea of all history, and they landed on the shore of glories, sins, and expiations.

Here Aeneas had landed with his ship, bringing the Trojan lares and penates to safety. The dying Augustus was deposited here. And here Tiberius and Agrippina had drowned in blood, if not in water.

For some time there had been a colony of believers in Pozzuoli, because almost every emigré from Asia or Africa made a stop here. They were converts in the Jewish-Christian tradition but they already knew the name of the Apostle to the Gentiles and may have read his letter to the Romans. They gave him a warm reception and wanted to keep him and his two companions for several days, which was granted by the good centurion. Meanwhile they sent messengers to the Roman brethren with the great announcement so that when Paul resumed his journey the first Roman brethren met him halfway, at that Market of Appius known as a den of bandits, though for Paul it proved a solicitous hospice. He found others at the Three Taverns (now known as Tre Taverne) some forty miles before Rome. Aquila and Prisca had preceded him to Rome, and they wanted to be the first to embrace him; perhaps there were also Alexander and Rufus, sons of Cyrenius, and Paul's childhood friends.

Thus happily finished the voyage of the prisoner who, with the soul of a conqueror, had come to Rome to submit to judgment. And this conquering soul was the greatest conqueror of souls ever to set foot in Latin land, nor would there be another such after him.

He was passing through the most pleasant and welcoming countryside he had yet known. Perhaps they showed him Seneca's luxurious villa on that road. He must certainly have known and respected the philosopher's severe wisdom and manly spirit even if he could not respect his overweening love

233

for possessions and creature comforts. There is a tradition that the philosopher wanted to meet the apostle, and went to visit him in prison, and that they exchanged the letters which are widely circulated under their names.

No harm in letting tradition tell a fine fable of example or a similitude take the place of a verity. The stoic school contained no announcement of Christian dogma, but it opened the door to Christian morality when it admonished men to listen to the voice of conscience, which might conceal within itself a most high being that no one knew. Tacitus, abhorring the vices of the proud and powerful but not correspondingly fond of the virtues of the wise and humble, could consider the stoics a sect designed only to create troublemakers and climbers (he was even more unjust and opposed to the Christians), but there is no doubt that the stoic school educated and tempered strong minds to virtue and was a constant force in preserving Rome from total decomposition. Seneca's *"res severa magnium gaudium"* could have been seconded by Paul.

Paul and Seneca may never have known each other, but it is not surprising that several church fathers also considered that exchange of letters authentic, for in them Seneca shows himself desirous of speaking to the Emperor on Paul's behalf, and the apostle does not lose hope that Seneca may become a disciple of Christ and, with his so eloquent wisdom, persuade, convert, or at least soften his friends, the Emperor's courtiers, or even the Emperor himself—"the word of God given to you could give birth to the new and uncorrupted man in them. . . ."

Rome in the spring of the year 61 A.D. was living through one of the gloomiest periods of history, a precipitous descent from bad to worse, as though bewitched by shadowy maleficence. Every evening the man who is still able to examine his conscience believes he has reached the bottom of the abyss, but the next day he wakes on the edge of a new bottomless abyss so that he falls into the final despair believing that there is no end to evil. It is then that he thinks Satan is invincible.

The whole world was going through this same period of moral disintegration, of horrors and terrors stamped with every vice, and with those virtues which can be secretly nourished in days dominated by the devil, since almost the whole of the known world was part of the Roman Empire. Misfortune is a gulf, and the people who fall therein follow the laws of falling bodies. But even in that despairing belief that there may be no end to the evil, faith is not completely extinguished, because everything that has a beginning must have an end. And it will be tomorrow, even if only to begin again.

Paul arrived in Rome to find the city in fear and ferment because of a notorious crime that had just occurred. The prefect of the city, Pedanius Secundus, had been killed by a slave, but the architect of the crime was not known. There were some who said that the master had denied his servant liberty after the slave had given him the price of his freedom, others that the slave, smitten by an adolescent girl, could not tolerate his master as rival for her affections. For one reason and another Pedanius was far from a saint, but ancient custom demanded that all the slaves living under his roof should be punished with the malefactor. Pedanius had four hundred slaves, and there were four hundred innocents to be killed. The people were in an uproar; the senate was hesitant before the execution of such slaughter. But a terrible example must be made to prevent a community of slaves from becoming accomplices of an assassin in the future, covering his misdeed with gang loyalty. An eloquent senator made a speech which convinced the hesitant.

"Today when there are people from every country among

our slaves, varying in their customs and strangers to our worship, deprived of every religion, only through fear can we control this hodgepodge. True, innocents also will die. But the same thing takes place in a dispersed army when the valiant, too, die under the rod in decimation. Every exemplary measure has some iniquity in it, but the sacrifice of the individual is the price of the common good."

The merciless sentence was carried out. A compact multitude tried to obstruct its execution with stones and torches, but the Emperor ordered two rows of soldiers aligned along the innocents' journey toward the place of execution. The usual zealot, who never flinches at evil, but is often absent from good, added that the freedmen in the house should also be condemned to deportation from Italy, but the Emperor did not accept the advice of the zealot, whose name was Cingonio Varrone. Justice is a twisted mask when it covers the face of fear.

Paul may not have reached Rome in time to be present at the dreadful spectacle, but he was told about it on his arrival. Roman justice was more benign with him. Taken to the Castro Praetorium—and at that time the prefect of the praetorium was one of the rare men of honor, Afrani Burrus—he was not kept prisoner because the magistrates realized when they read the Caesarean procurator's report that according to Roman law there was no crime to be expiated; Paul had only to wait for an audience with the Emperor. During that wait, which could have been long indeed and as it was lasted for two years, he was kept in military custody but left free to rent a house, to receive friends, and to move about the city. Protective custody rather than prison, he was obliged only to keep a guardian angel constantly at his side, chained left arm to right arm.

Good company if a bit heavy, because after all soldiers are good sorts, common people but often useful and helpful company; even though, for a man of prayer and thought, solitude is the highest good. But Paul was the man to achieve that good even with an extraneous object attached to his body, an object who moved with him, rested with him, listened to his words, and almost breathed his very breath.

29

"To Live Is Christ"

For some time now the Jews had been established in that great harbor where the deities of every religion, Serapis, Isis, Cybele, Mithras, and so on had already taken residence. There were about twenty to thirty thousand Jews in Rome, grouped in about ten synagogues, with their own officers of the law, as in every country, and the power to issue decrees.

The first Jews were the slaves brought back as booty of war by Palestine's conquerors a century earlier. From these slaves, other slaves were born, laboring flesh trained to raise the enormous walls of the aqueducts, the theaters, the baths, block upon block. A continuous influx of immigrants had followed on the slaves' heels; dammed for a while by Claudius' edict, it had resumed its flow when Nero reopened Rome, and even the gates of his palace, to the Jews. For the most part they were ordinary people, from merchants, peddlers, brokers, to those who dealt in all kinds of petty business, odd jobs, and spells. They were first camped at the city's outskirts and later gathered together to exercise their minute trades in Trastevere, between

Isola Tiberina and Gianiculum. Romans never penetrated into their domain.

But traffickers of another kind, too, existed, people who had come in the wake of the favored Herods and had insinuated themselves into the court, a herd of actors, astrologers, and mathematicians whose jests and flattery wiled away the Emperor's idle hours. An Alitino, histrionic and buffoon, had become the most celebrated actor in the imperial theater. Poppaea Sabine protected the historian Flavius Josephus and always loved to have a band of Jewish serving maids in attendance, to listen to their imaginative conversation and their mournful songs; she was said to harbor the secret whim of joining their religion.

The Christians were a small group which had grown around the first nuclei come from Pozzuoli and Ostia. They were not ex-Jews but, ignorant of the Mosaic Law and the rites of the temple, were chiefly pagans who had heeded the centurion Cornelius and those who spoke of him. Some may also have come in contact with Alexander and Rufus, the sons of Cyrenius, those two missionaries known only by name and not by word or act who appear and disappear here and there for thirty years, wandering lights in the century's fog, always eluding the grasp of history.

If Peter had already been there, he had not obliged them to follow the rites of the synagogue and obey the Law, because the apostle who had not denied the centurion baptism appreciated the benefits of peace and concord above all. Peter was wary only of Paul's excessive polemic ardor, and he feared the possible extravagances of his disciples, who were inspired to exaggerate their master's doctrine. Peter, who understood best the language of the heart, was wont to say of the Pauline letters only that they contained things difficult to understand.

Having no great teachers, this Roman community had

grown up apart from schools, in the language of the heart, which specially teaches the practice of the great Christian virtues. Aquila and Priscilla had returned a couple of years before to their house on the Aventine, and they spread the Good News from there.

They were attended by souls bruised and wounded by the daily impact with vice and crime which during the past thirty years had transformed Rome into a theater of horrors. Mithras, the warrior, pleased the soldiers; Christ, the Crucified, appealed to the slaves, the afflicted, the rejected. Tired of the vain struggle against the assault of evil, their consciences found rest by withdrawing from what are commonly called worldly interests.

Women especially—and Rome still held women of signal virtue—sought out those Christian voices, they repeated them in their hearts, confided in them like a secret of love and hope, made them a prayer and dedication. Misfortune washes the spirit of the mud of rage and grays and, out of sorrow, refinement of soul flowers. In oppressed and devastated families, just as in the families of the oppressors and devastators, the spirit of insufferance and the spirit of repentance became entwined to form an aura of sweet abnegation, of indifference to danger, of dedication to an unknown and highest ideal. The Roman women saw the chastity of the Christian maidens and the respect of the men who honored that chaste way of life as a mark of enviable and happy superiority. The Virgin resisted Venus.

Then illustrious ladies and unknown slavegirls were seen to turn to the new preachers of God, with the trepidation of one who follows a glimmering taper into the darkness of a cavern. Veiled matrons appeared in the believers' secret meetings. The beautiful slave Acte, who was the Emperor's first love and later discarded and scorned, was already a Christian. She loved her horrendous mad lover until the end and arranged his body in the sepulcher with her own hands. Christians gathered in the Annea family where she served. The wife of Aulus Plautius, conqueror of Gaul, Pomponia Grecina, who was a woman famous for her constancy and rectitude of character according to Tactitus, was accused of "foreign superstition" and handed over to her husband for judgment in accordance with ancient custom. He declared her innocent, and for forty years she led a strict and retired life. She always wore black. In addition to the sorrow of family deaths, people said that she bore in her heart "mysterious hopes," perhaps. The daughters of the senator Pudente, Prassede and Pudenziana were also of Christian inclination, along with many other matrons and maids.

It was the widespread expectation of a heavenly gift which would soothe sorrow and transmute weeping into sweet joy. It was the contagious yearning after "mysterious hopes." An aura of melancholy hovered over many Roman houses, that melancholy which exudes like a mystic elevation from every ruin and forms an aura of sanctity around mishap and ill doing. Intimation of weeping, and these Christians knew how to weep as the Latin people never wept. It was not the faith yet, but the preparation was there.

Paul wasted no time about getting into action. He had not come to Rome for recreation: he was a prisoner but a voluntary one, with the intention of accomplishing the mission assigned in his vision at Caesarea, to achieve the goal of his sojourn on earth. He sent his young comrades out to distribute an invitation, and on the third day a gathering of Jews met in the prison of his house.

They knew him only by name. They had heard talk about his sect and his doctrines but had not given it importance. Paul spoke but he convinced no one. They listened and shrugged their shoulders and returned to their workshops and business. They had already had their troubles with Claudius; they wanted none with Nero. And Paul said and did at Rome, too, what he usually said and did every time he presented himself before a synagogue: "I have done my duty with you; now I shall speak to the Gentiles."

But he was certainly sincere in doing his duty. Until the last day there was always the bitterness in his heart of being perpetually misunderstood and slandered and insulted among his own people. The victory over the Gentiles may not have repaid that lofty soul athirst for truth from the perpetual war waged on him by the Jews. The Jews hated him to the death, but he never hated, and he fought in them the rigid formalisms of his own native people. In the process of gathering money for Jerusalem he had already written to the Romans: "If the Gentiles have come to share with them in things spiritual, they are under a debt to minister to them in things carnal." The Gentiles must repay with worldly goods the spiritual values received from the Jews.

Paul's propaganda had a wildfire success with the Gentiles at Rome. His chains aided him. It is not pleasant, it is a constant harassment, the company of an outsider who never leaves you for an instant, a body attached to your body, more insistent than your own shadow, but that enforced company was of benefit to Paul, who knew how to be alone with his thoughts and with God.

The praetorian guard attached to him was changed every evening. Often they were curious, for the prisoner was a truly extraordinary person who roused the curiosity of even the most coarse and vicious man. Mild, sober, generous, he gave of himself completely. Weak and emaciated like a starving man, he was made of steel in his resistance to effort and sleeplessness. When he spoke there was such an imperious light on that balding, high forehead, and yet he was so restrained and modest in the hours of repose. He was like no other prisoner, criminal or innocent though he might be. He was like no other man of power, so many of whom were to be seen at Rome, emperors and their favorites, generals, consuls, prefects, orators, courtiers, poets, and possessors of boundless riches. And he spoke as one can think that the gods speak.

Paul told his Gospel to every guard. When their turn came up again, the soldiers who had not laughed or forgotten, wanted to know more. The first converts of Jesus and virtue came from among the lost souls of the praetorians. Then every converted praetorian brought the yeast of that renewal to his family, to the markets, and to social occasions.

Happy days for the prisoner. After the first days in Antioch with his beloved Barnabas, beautiful days which had been the dawn of the growing religion, and of others in full noon in Lydia's house in Philippi, this was perhaps the most serene and active time of Paul's life. The prisoner's room became a family chapel. He divided his days in periods of three hours each, keeping a short intermission of prayer between each part. The young disciples who had accompanied him now helped him to bear his chains sometimes, and the soldier of the guard did not object. Better yet, free to move about, they helped bear his words where he could not go. From the praetorian legions the Gospel penetrated the wider world of slaves, more miserable and more open to heavenly hopes. The hecatombs in the house of the prefect Pedanius had prepared this opening for him.

Luke, Aristarchus, and Timothy never left him during the whole period of imprisonment and trial. Many others came to join them. Epaphras and Tychicus of Ephesus, Epaphroditus of Philippi, a Jesus called the Just, a Demas, Phygellus, and Hermogenes. Every church he had founded wanted to send one of its elders to bring him the news he asked so anxiously and the help he did not ask. As always Philippi was the most solicitous, and Lydia sent him more money than he needed. But some money he did need, for with chains on his arm he was no longer able to work at the loom.

They were obedient and industrious men who put themselves at the indefatigable apostle's disposition, like soldiers loyal to their captain. That rouser of energies multiplied the effectiveness of his followers. He was right to praise them as "brothers, cooperators, and companions in struggle." Epaphroditus fell seriously ill, and Paul was his doctor and solicitous nurse. When he had cured him, he sent him back to his dear Philippians with the recommendation and prayer that they receive him joyfully and comfort his convalescence.

A slave came too, Onesimus, and asked his pardon and safety. He had fled from his master Philemon of Colossa to escape the punishment that awaited him for offending his master. He had ventured over land and sea in search of the apostle, who made him a Christian. He threw himself at his feet and begged to be allowed to stay with him. Paul took him in and welcomed him. He would willingly have kept him since the young man could have been most helpful, but it was not legal to take a slave away from his master. He sent him back to Philemon but gave him a charming letter of admonishment and entreaty for his master: "I plead with thee for this my child whom I have begotten in my bondage, Onesimus, a man once worthless to thee, but now of great worth, to thee as well as to me. Him have I sent back to thee, even him that is my very heart. I could have wished to keep him with me, that on thy behalf he might minister to me in my bonds for the Gospel. But I have determined to do nothing without thy consent, that thy good deed may not come of compulsion but of thy free will. Perhaps for this very reason he hath been separated from thee for a time, that thou mayest receive him as thine for ever, no longer as a slave, but as better than a slave, a beloved brother, especially to me, but how much more to thee both in the flesh and in the Lord. If then thou dost hold me thine in fellowship, receive him as thou wouldst myself. And if he hath wronged thee in any way, or oweth aught to thee, charge it to me."

The prayer of one who knows he is able to command.

It was only natural that the news from Asia and Macedonia should get worse, because when the architect is away it is in the logic of the young to introduce their own additions and touches into the master's plan, touches that are not always opportune and often deforming. The churches Paul had founded were no longer his; they were losing the stamp of his genius; still damp clay was transformed by the fingers of the last to handle it. It was inevitable that little centers of personal vanity and small tyrannies should develop. The new believers were growing in numbers, but calculation and scheming succeeded the first candid feelings. Especially in Asia, the first heresies were taking root among the cracks of the early unity. Phrygia always offered the most fertile ground for the rooting of religious propaganda. The flowering of little churches which had radiated from the church of Ephesus founded by Paul continued, the work of others now who kept themselves linked to Ephesus as the offshoot is connected to the trunk. The little city of Colossa had been destroyed by an earthquake but its church was not dead; it transferred first to Hierapolis and to Laodicea and then returned to the rebuilt city. A wind of holiness blew in that fertile, smiling valley. In just those days the slave's son Epictetus was born in Hierapolis, and here, too, in the new century the first church fathers would rise out of the heresies' corruption.

For those who are far away and awaiting news the passing days are like years, certainly the apostle, restricted by his captivity, must have been constantly harassed by the thought of his faraway churches. Writing letters could be a momentary distraction; it did not diminish his anxiety. He wrote to his friends in Colossa, in Ephesus, and in Philippi and sent the letters with Epaphras, Tychicus and Epaphroditus. He sent Timothy, too, to Philippi.

He did not write in his most forceful style. His scorn had been softened by sorrow, the asperity had become heartfelt ruefulness. After so much voyaging by land and sea, after so much agitation and anguish, his spirit had been soothed and uplifted to certainty. The present days could bring him storms of fear and disappointment, but the future was full of light. In his prison's shelter he found himself and his greatness again. No human force could destroy what he had built. Even if his churches went astray, the spirit he had infused in them remained incorrupt and eternal.

Some disciples deserted him too, and he felt neither sorrow nor anger. He had already written, "When I am weak, then am I strong." Now he knew himself strong beyond any human power.

The three letters he wrote shortly before being liberated are in part theoretical, in part ethical. In the dogmatic part of these letters Pauline theology reaches its highest level of clarity and brightness—the extreme sublimation of his thinking, it burns like a white flame. In the moral part he dwells on the praise of conjugal love and the exercise of all the family virtues with a gentleness and kindness which were missing from the preceding letters' excitement.

As he writes, his native polemic pride dwindles by itself to a more modest and moving apology because he is more sure of himself. Especially to his cherished Philippians, who lavished gifts and love on him, does he confide himself. He exhorts them insistently to gladness, with accents which only Francis of Assisi will achieve twelve centuries later.

Gently, he reminds them of what he has done for them.

247

"For the rest, brethren, all that is true, all that is seemly, all that is just, all that is pure, all that is lovable, all that is winning —whatever is virtuous or praiseworthy—let such things fill your thought. What ye have learnt and received and heard and seen in me, put that into practice, and the God of peace shall be with you."

To them he entrusts his last wish: "For with me to live is Christ and to die is gain. But if to live in the flesh meaneth for me fruitful labor—then, which I am to choose I cannot tell. I am caught between the two; my longing to set forth and to be with Christ—for that were far better—yet for your sakes to remain in the flesh is more needful. And indeed I am quite persuaded that remain I shall, and remain close beside you all, for your progress and joy in the faith, and that ye may have abundant ground in me for boasting in Christ Jesus, through my presence once more among you."

30

Rome Burns

About that time Peter, too, came to Rome, and he was followed by apostles and disciples, John, Mark, Barnabas, and others. The river of history's course is determined by the political and social conditions of the terrain through which it flows. The bearers of the new religion realized, or felt, that the river which sprang from the sources of Jerusalem and Antioch must have its mouth at Rome. And if all the roads of men led to Rome, the road of God would depart from there.

In every other church around the Mediterranean the followers of the two schools could work separately and contend with one another, because life is born out of contention too: at Rome it was necessary to work together in agreement.

Paul's arrival in Rome worried Peter a little, not so much because of the apostle's activity, bound by his chains, but because of that of his enterprising disciples. It may be that the group of Judeo-Christians which saw Paul's mission among the Gentiles growing and spreading wanted its leader and called Peter for re-enforcement. Why not believe, too, the pretty fable which makes Peter the tireless pursuer of Simon Magus from country to country all the way to the capital, where the sorcerer had come to exercise his spells, there to confute and crush the counterfeiter of Christianity. And history has predestined causes that men try in vain to discover. Peter was the foundation stone of the new religion, chosen by Jesus, and Rome was the capital of the world.

The two apostles lived in separate places, far from each other. Paul's pagan followers had no meeting place except their master's prison-house and were scattered throughout the city, many of them in the court's upper and lower strata, among the masters and slaves. Peter's converted Jews were huddled at Porta Portese, a remote vineyard between the Gianiculum and the Vatican, beyond the gardens of Nero.

The two leaders, one free and the other chained, certainly wanted to see each other, and it is reasonable to think that Peter went to see Paul in his voluntary prison and that Paul joyously received in his sanctified shelter the elder apostle, most direct heir to Jesus' thinking.

Far from Jerusalem, no longer weighed down by the heavy aura of their millenary Hebrew inheritance, the two great heralds certainly felt their kinship and agreement. Inevitably they had suffered from sibling rivalry, but without acrimony. It was not enough to forget the harsh disagreement at Antioch with one's mind; it must be erased from the heart.

Now they were both old, one more so than the other, and both had labored much. Paul recognized the generous fisherman of Bethsaida's talents and authority. Paul had the strength of genius, the other the virtues of the heart. And Peter could not but feel the magnetic attraction of his great rival, so much more audacious and cultivated than himself. In the long afternoons of the idle Roman summer, and perhaps through the long winter nights too, while the most cynical and obscene carnival ever staged by great Babylon raged and raved around them, the old fisherman skirted the Tiber's meanders and came across the whole city to visit the learned prisoner in his house down at the foot of the Coelian Hill, in a noisy shopkeepers' quarter where no one would have suspected the little temple's existence. They kept each other company. They spoke together of their hopes. Peter also told Paul of the events and works of Jesus' life, repeated the Master's words which he retained in his prodigious memory, and asked Paul to explain obscure passages in his theology, especially in the letter written to the Romans, which was now variously interpreted by the Romans. They tried not to contradict each other: at the end each one remained "in the kind of teaching he had received."

Sometimes Peter was accompanied by John Mark, the disciple who had left Paul to go back to Peter, and whose companionship the offended Paul had later refused. Many years had gone by, and that anger, too, had fallen away, leaving Paul with a sentiment of respect and affection for the virtuous and cultivated younger man. Sometimes Paul's disciples, too, returned from their missions in the city and remained to listen to the masters' conversation.

Perhaps at this time Mark and Luke wrote their Gospels, retiring to their own rooms while their masters were resting and meditating, first the one, then a little later the other. Mark's all full of tales from Peter; Luke inclined through long familiarity to follow Paul's thinking and, like Paul, to address himself to the Gentiles. Mark left for Asia, charged with a mission for Peter, and Paul gave him letters of introduction to his friends.

Only John, son of Zebedee, the once youthful disciple of Christ who was now aged himself, lived outside the Pauline circle and was untouched by the flame of that eloquence which had scattered so much fire around the Mediterranean. He lived as though closed in an armor of invulnerable independence.

251

Jesus' favorite disciple guarded his native sweetness in a sense of proud and prickly solitude as though he wanted to preserve the Master's gift of predilection within that armor.

Peter also decided to write a letter to the Asian believers about that time for he, too, was afflicted by their controversies. Especially addressing himself to the Jews "that sojourn in the dispersion," he wrote a gentle letter admonishing them to modesty, chastity, and love of one's neighbors, the letter of a very good man of scanty education. He knew that women, particularly, believed in him and his most persuasive expression was directed to them.

"Let not your adornment be outward," he wrote, "in the plaiting of the hair, or in the use of jewelry, or in the wearing of dress; but let it be the hidden life of the heart, in the imperishable meekness and peace of the Spirit, which is precious in the sight of God." And this strong image addressed to the men is his: "Be ye sober and watch. Your adversary the devil goeth about like a roaring lion seeking to devour. . . ."

The faraway echo of Christ's words breathing the odor of the lake of Tiberias and the fields of Capharnaum is felt in every sentence, but the rumbling echo of the closer words of Paul, attended in those very days, is also to be heard. He confessed he had not understood everything in Paul's letters but he read them attentively, and he has not forgotten what he did understand. The whole letter is fashioned in the Pauline stamp. Some concepts are taken unaltered from the letters to the Romans and the Corinthians. Others, too, will try to imitate Paul: the Tarsian's eloquence enthralled even those who opposed and feared him.

Peter then wrote a second letter. By the time he had been freed from his chains and absolved by Nero's tribunal, Paul had already left Rome.

While they were together, their propaganda found a meeting point particularly in teaching submission to power. It was a way of life not entirely in accordance with their principles but politically necessary if the battle was not to be lost even before the forces were ready to fight. They both insisted on it in their letters to those far away, and certainly they made it the object of lessons and recommendations to those near by.

It was necessary. Living in its midst, they saw every day the dangers facing the growing church in Rome, and the face of the monster appeared without veils or masks in all the horror of its satanic bestiality. They were walking on the edge of a pit full of boiling tar, and one false step was enough to slip into it. The effects of the two missions were often in opposition. Paul made mild and obedient disciples among the pagans; already resigned or at least accustomed to submission, they escaped into religious rapture. The Jews converted by Peter remained dangerously untamed. It was necessary to calm these agitated spirits who carried their faith into politics with the characteristic excesses of their temperament.

The Roman people, who had first defended the weaker Christians against the outspoken and troublesome Jews, now found the Christians, too, quite troublesome since they had become so numerous, a *"multitudo ingens."* They tolerated them unwillingly, ridiculed their humility, suspected their sober living as false and mean, and made fun of their mystic exaltation. Finally they, too, were disgusted by the savage spectacles of the circus and felt sympathy for the Christian gentiles who shunned those horrors in open disapproval. Then with a surprising but not inexplicable reversal of a collective state of whirling disorientation, they shifted and decided that these same Christians, educated to abstinence and alien to bloodshed, were capable of every crime and horror.

Because the Orient sent to Rome people from Syria, Phrygia, and Cappadocia, in addition to Jews and Christians, and poured out all kinds of filth and fakery from Asia to be added to the Christian religion, the Roman people made one great confusion of people, rites, and customs. Balbillus, the Ephesian astrologer and mathematician who had come to enlighten Nero, strutted about in Rome with his lurid doings. The wizard of Gitton was said to have planted his booth of spells and sortilege in the great fair of Rome after dragging it through all the markets of Asia. It was logical that the confusion and hallucinated excitement, produced by the daily spectacle of abominations and the daily terror of worse abomination, should lead the people into persecuting mania. It was less logical, and to us it seems almost unbelievable, that educated people sustained by reason should all err in the same way. They accused the Christians of crimes never committed, of procuring and strangling little children, poisoning fountains, sowing the evil eye. They made fun of them, carrying a figure of Jesus with the head of a donkey about with them and using it as an emblem of attack at the entrance to Christian houses. They even said that the crime was in the use of the name.

The missionaries of neighborly love, including an enemy neighbor, were considered "haters of humankind" even by Tacitus, who described the Christian religion as "execrable superstition" and the believers as people capable of every shameful and wicked action, a guilty breed deserving of new examples of punishment. It did not require a singular effort of imagination for Nero to accuse the Christians of setting the fire at Rome nor an effort of mind for the people to believe it, even though the "new example" of punishment seems excessive to the historian himself.

Even after twenty centuries the description of that novel punishment is repugnant in a holy tale. In history and fiction so much ink has been used to paint the picture of those in-

254

credible atrocities that it would be an arduous, as well as useless, effort to seek blacker and filthier descriptive adjectives. We who have seen the unbelievable crimes of the concentration camps in our own century, with prisoners unrecognizably altered in torture chambers, with ovens to bake not bread but living men, we who know of millions of victims immolated to the divinity of a herd of monsters made in the human image; we can picture Neronian spectacles in our imagination without reading or writing, and presage the approach of the final evening.

The perversion, the cruelty, the perfidy, and the lie had the face then, as they have today, of the Beast, of Satan, of the Antichrist. And innocence showed its virgin countenance dehumanized by terror, as we, too, have seen it. And where today the torture has been perfected by science, there it was refined by esthetics. The saplings immersed first in oil so that they would flame more rapidly as living torches, the rod driven into the human trunk till it came out of the mouth, the barbarous myth of Pasiphae raped by a bull and the Dirce virgins dragged, beaten, and torn asunder on the horns of other enraged bulls, provided sport for the Emperor, the court, and the people for several days, first in the circus, then in the gardens of Nero.

Peter may have died the death of almost all his disciples, nailed under an overturned cross.

John miraculously escaped the cauldron of boiling oil being prepared for him outside Porta Maggiore and found shelter in Asia.

Paul had been gone for a year.

31

History and Poesy

Paul went free from Rome, and the historian loses track of him at this point. The missionary continued his mission, and he was in a hurry, knowing that not many years of life remained to him. He was almost sixty years old, and if not old, he had, however, journeyed so much that life already seemed as long as the roads he traveled; he had worn himself out beyond the strength bestowed on him by God: he was approaching his last day on earth. But until that day he must travel and struggle and suffer. He had said all he had to say, but he had not said it to all.

The historian loses sight of the apostle. Paul withdraws and vanishes in the face of our desire to follow his every step, our eager curiosity to know his heart in his last years. We have the painful deception of waking up one morning and no longer finding at our side the great companion who has guided and sustained us in this our work. Paul, the severe and gentle father, has abandoned us.

But the father never really abandons his children. What

does the existence of a man who has already supplied his earthly labor to the chronicle of human events matter now? Paul had been acquitted; the Emperor's decree freed him from the chains of the praetorian guard, and he can take up his pack and staff to journey over land and sea; he can write, preach, suffer, see his children again, but we can no longer know for a certainty where he goes and what he does. He no longer belongs to history. The poetry of legend has taken possession of him even before the great divide.

History and legend go together to seek a ray of light in the forest of myths and evidence. They come upon prints which seem to have been stamped by his feet and follow those prints which lead them here and there, toward faraway poles, and where the prints stop the searchers stop too; but Paul is no longer there, he has left on other missions.

They hear a voice which is certainly Paul's voice. That voice says words unmistakably spoken or written by him. They follow the echoes of those words, their faraway reverberations, and arrive at their source, but already Paul is no longer there; his words remain suspended in the air, stretching toward other shores.

Paul's footsteps are met in all the lands around the Mediterranean except Egypt; Paul's voice resounds in all the skies above the Mediterranean. And in every city one meets an old man who has seen him pass, a woman who has helped him with a sip of water and some bread, an enemy who has denounced him to the magistrate, a youth who wanted to follow him but was ordered to wait for his return.

Did he not go directly to Spain from Rome? Who forbids us to believe that he traveled to the end of his pre-established path? It was the final goal marked in his trip to the West; he wanted to reach the limits of the world before dying, and God would have granted him his desire because he deserved it. Perhaps he made a stop in Marseilles where a frail young offshoot of the new faith was already flourishing; then on his return he ventured forth into the vast Mediterranean and, now free, reached the isle of Crete which he had barely glimpsed as a prisoner on his first trip to Rome. Why should he not have stopped several months on the island to found another church there? He will have left Titus on Crete and continued on through Greece and Asia. Was he able to see his churches in Macedonia and Galatia again? His final smile and final sob. He will have gone further, all the way to Nicopolis on the Adriatic. They will have imprisoned him again and brought him back to Rome in chains. In these years, he wrote another letter, one of his longest, and sent it to the Jews in Jerusalem. Legend has gotten possession of that letter, and history says it is hers. What matter the vain contest?

James was dead, and with James fell the great bulwark of the church at Jerusalem. Disorder took over in the cradle of the Christian religion, where the holy city's supreme catastrophe was already in preparation.

Broken was the bond which kept Jews and Christians united in the prestige and conciliating spirit of the Lord's brotherhood. The Jews became persecutors again, and the Christians stiffened in their zeal. But more than ever zealots, those Christians did not forget that they were also Jews, and they attached themselves more closely to the Mosaic Law. Left to itself, Christianity in Jerusalem was on the verge of falling back into Mosaicism. It was then that the sect of the Ebionites became strong and preached the most rigorous respect for the Law together with strictest poverty.

Why should the letter to the Hebrews written to dam up the dispersal of Christian belief not be Paul's work? In it the dogma of Jesus, Author and Mediator of the new alliance, superior to Moses, the mediator of the old alliance, is expressed in definitive fashion, though with unusually soft and impersonal words. It is the essence of Paul's thought.

Criticism and tradition do not agree in conceding to history the possession of this letter, but without rivalry, since neither of the two is fully convinced of its rightness and reasoning. Can the author of the letter have more importance than its argument? The spirit of the letter is completely Pauline, so it does not matter that the words may have been another's work. Perhaps the theme was dictated to one of his young secretaries who developed it himself. Perhaps one of those youths wrote it of his own initiative, remembering his master's teaching, as the best homage he could offer. Barnabas may have written it, or some other learned man fed on Paul's thinking who was more ignorant of Greek than Barnabas.

Did Paul come back to Rome in chains like the first time to undergo another trial, or free and haughty to encounter prison there? Of the walls and vaults constructed by him for his churches in Asia he had found only heaps of stone. This is life: make, unmake, remake. He knew that those scattered stones would come together and reunite by themselves to form new constructions. He knew that the heaps of stones would become cathedrals. But he realized that he must bring new stones to Rome to bring it about, for only in Rome was the new church in a position to find unity and become solidly established. They were the stones of supreme martyrdom, and they had been borne by Peter and by the youths who were a part of Nero's persecution.

How much time, poesy asks, did Paul spend in Rome before dying there? Did he live in his own house in the Arenula quarter next to the Tiber or was he immediately thrown into the underground dungeons of the Tullian prison? Prisoners came into the light of the sun from there only to be consigned to death, by crucifixion, decapitation, or the jaws of the beasts in the circus. Paul felt that he, too, must undergo martyrdom before reaching God. In the midst of so much death among youth, how unjust that he, already old, should survive.

"To live is Christ," he had written a little earlier to the Philippians, "to die is gain." And he did not know which to choose because his life was still necessary for others and dying of benefit only to himself. Now his words and his works had accomplished their cycle. Now he could do no more with his life, and so he would do it with his death. After the teaching, the example. Now the choice was made: no longer life, Christ.

The dungeon was not so closed and dark that every now and then a crack in the tomblike stone did not open to let in a disciple or a ray of light. A spiritual son from the churches of Macedonia and Asia still came, a missive from faraway brethren sending him prayers and gifts, a young woman bringing him food or newly-washed clothing. The horrible spectacle of the persecution had not entirely extinguished the new faith among the soldiers and jailers, enraptured souls who also faced martyrdom so as not to betray the secret.

But from day to day the cracks of light become thinner and sparser, the shadows blacker. Like history, many comrades also deserted him, tired of suffering and unworldliness. A man like Paul is destined to end his life alone. Alone with his idea, alone with his truth, alone with God. Jesus, too, was alone, separated from His disciples on the night of Gethsemane.

There were those at his trial who were unable to defend him so as not to incur the same punishment, a Phygellus, a Hermogenes, a Hymenaeus, and an Alexander the coppersmith. This Alexander was another Judas who testified against Paul. Luke did not desert him, nor did Onesiphorus, who had sought so far through the streets of Rome to find him. A woman named Claudia came to visit him up to the final day, and the senator Pudens, and Linus, who may have become Peter's successor. He had left Timothy in Asia and now he ardently desired him as a man might want his dearest son beside his deathbed. He also would have liked to see Mark again.

And the others? Barnabas will die, possibly victim of a personal vendetta on his native island of Cyprus. Aquila and Apollos go back into the shadows.

Paul had already written a first letter to Timothy while he was on his way to Rome as he had also written to Titus; awaiting his trial he wrote the former a second letter. They are the letters of a sad and serene man who rests a moment on the verge of his final step and directs his gaze to the streets of the earth before being forever separated from them and raising his eyes to the infinite. He imparts his final counsels and admonitions.

Let the young persevere and "fight the good fight, holding to faith and a good conscience." They should study how to show themselves worthy of God's approval, "a laborer unshamed, handling aright the word of truth." They should "charge those who are rich in this present world not to be haughty, or set their hope on the uncertainty of riches, but on God, who provideth us richly with all things unto enjoyment thereof; to do good, to be rich in good works, to be openhanded and generous." They should respect the aged and not correct them harshly if they sin but beg them to improve themselves as a son exhorts his father "and young men as brothers, elderly women as mothers, younger women as sisters in all chastity. Honor widows, who are truly widowed. If any widow hath children or grandchildren, let these first learn to practice godliness toward those at home and to make some return to their parents; for this is acceptable in the sight of God."

Especially he demands loftiness of soul, irreproachable ways and open charity of those who are placed in the forefront as church leaders. He has been the initiator: when the guests come to live in the new houses and become masters therein, then will the new houses truly begin to live. "A bishop, then, must be irreproachable, married but once, temperate, self-controlled, orderly, hospitable, a capable teacher: not given to tippling or brawling, but considerate, peaceable, not a lover of money: a good ruler of his own household, keeping his children in subjection and all reverence (if indeed a man knoweth not how to rule his own household, how is he to take care of the church of God?)" Knowing well that dissensions which later become heresies often have their origin in personal enmities, he severely condemns those who in exercising their religious ministry are unable to acquire a good reputation with outsiders.

In the last letter to his most cherished disciple he gives way to a moment of disheartenment, and the fear of the abysses about to open in the world spurts from his heart. "But know this, that in the last days grievous times will set in. For men will be selfish, covetous, boastful, haughty, railers, disobedient to parents, ungrateful, unholy, unloving, implacable, slanderers, dissolute, unbridled, no lovers of good, treacherous, headstrong, besotted with pride, lovers of pleasure rather than of God, with a semblance of piety, but repudiating the living force thereof. Such as these do thou ward off. For of these are they that make their way into houses, and take captive silly women who are laden with sins and led about by manifold lust. . . ."

The last flaming of the apostle's burning eloquence. And it was necessary because this is the last time that he writes to the favorite among all his apostles, his rightful heir who will be his life in the world, to the true son of his heart and thought. He knows he is entrusting him with a deposit difficult to guard, an enormous charge which would crush frailer shoulders. "You are young, Timothy, but shun the stupid and useless disputes which generate quarrels, because a servant of God should not bicker, but leave the quarrels to the zealots of mutilation.

"Remind men of these things, adjuring them before God to avoid controversy, which serveth no good purpose, but maketh for the ruin of the hearers. Strive earnestly to present thyself to God as a man approved, a laborer unshamed, handling aright the word of truth. But profane babblings avoid, for those who indulge therein will go farther and farther in impiety, and their word will spread like cancer . . .

"But flee youthful lusts; pursue rather justness, faith, charity, peace with those that call upon the Lord out of a pure heart. Avoid foolish and uneducated discussions, knowing they beget quarrels; a servant of the Lord must not quarrel, but on the contrary be gentle towards all.

"But thou hast noted well my teaching, my manner of life, my aims, my faith, my long suffering, my charity, my patience, my persecutions, my sufferings . . . all that will to live piously in Christ Jesus shall be persecuted . . . do thou abide in those things whereof thou has been instructed and convinced, mindful from whom thou didst learn them.

"Preach the word, be urgent in season and out of season, reprove, rebuke, exhort, with all long suffering and instruction . . . suffer hardship . . . fulfill thy ministry.

"As for me, already I am poured out in sacrifice, and the time of my departure is at hand. I have fought the good fight, I have accomplished the course, I have kept the faith."

In the first letter he coddled him with maternal tenderness. "Drink no longer water only, but use a little wine, on account of thy stomach and the frequent illnesses."

And now, let him come quickly to Rome where there is no one but Luke to keep the apostle company. Make haste, Timothy, make haste if the master is to be found alive. And bring the cape he left at Troas, in Carpus' house, and the books, particularly the parchments. He has nothing to read in prison and not even writing materials. And he is very cold. . . .

Timothy brought him the mantle and the books and the parchment, but he may not have found him alive, may not have seen his master again.

The Emperor's first tribunal had absolved Paul of any crime against Rome: the second tribunal condemned Paul as guilty of all the crimes of the Christians, subverters of the laws and morals of the Empire. He was sentenced to decapitation.

We would like to see him again. Our affectionate curiosity asks the poesy of legend to let us find him one last time. And legend shows him beheaded one summer morning on the road to Ostia in a solitary place called the Waters of Sage.

32

The Last Apostle

The chief pillar of Jerusalem, James, was already dead. Stoned like Stephen; then a wool carder finished him off with a cudgel.

The high priest Anaias, another Anaias, son of the first Anaias who had crucified Jesus, condemned and killed Jesus' cousin James. He had intervened in the brief period between the departure of the Roman procurator Festus and the arrival of his successor Albinus, usurping the Emperor's power, and had promulgated the illegal sentence. When Albinus arrived, he re-established the authority of Roman law and dismissed those who had violated it. In a few years, the detested Anaias was to die and his corpse would remain unburied. The dynasty of the Anaias family ended with this last high priest. It was the beginning of the end of the temple.

This was in the year 62 A.D. James was 97 years old. Before he died he, too, had written a letter directed to all the communities of Jews converted to Christianity. It may have been suggested by Paul's letter because he repeated several of Paul's themes to reach opposite conclusions. But it was not a polemic letter; in fact it corresponded in every expression to the writer's character, reflective and of tranquil firmness.

The acrimony and argumentativeness were only in his followers' zeal. And the followers put into their propaganda animosity and pettiness that were not in their leader's spirit. He wanted to leave a written record of his thinking on the disagreement in existence for twenty years between the faith and its works. He was not rigidly formal but humanly close to reality, and even Paul, who always places the revivifying spirit before the destroying letter, could have endorsed it.

"What availeth it, my brethren, if anyone say that he hath faith, yet hath not works? Can his faith save him? If a brother or a sister be naked, or in want of daily food, and any one of you say to them, 'Go in peace, warm and fill yourselves,' and do not give them the things that are needful for the body what availeth it? So also faith, if it have not works, is dead in itself. But someone will say, 'Thou has faith and I have works.' Show me thy faith without the works, and I from my works will show thee my faith. . . . See ye that a man is justified through works, and not through faith alone? . . . For as the body without the spirit is dead, so also faith without works is dead."

It is the most evangelical of the apostles' letters. Even more than Peter's two letters is this letter of James close to Jesus, whose lofty and allusive way of expressing himself in parabolas, antitheses, and figures of speech he often repeats, even to the words, that lyric improvisation drawing from every aspect of nature, trees, flowers, and birds. In this letter the permeating echo of the Sermon on the Mount is heard, as if in synthesis. Especially the praise of poverty and the aversion to riches remained in old James's heart, and he re-echoes them with the asperity of many years lived among greedy priests and starving beggars.

268

"Come now, ye rich; weep and lament over the woes which are coming upon you. Your wealth hath wasted away and your garments are becoming moth-eaten, your gold and silver are rusted, and the rust thereof shall be in witness against you, and it shall feed upon your flesh like as fire. Ye have laid up treasure against the last days." He, too, restates Jesus' admonition to plain speaking. "But before all things, my brethren, swear ye not, neither by heaven, nor by the earth, nor by any other oath; but let your Yea be Yea, and your Nay Nay. . . ."

They were words that had become proverbial in Palestine, and all the compilers of the Gospel put them down.

Shut up in Jerusalem, where every stone repeated the Master's words, James had been able to live intimately with his memories. Possibly a remote and inattentive disciple of the living Jesus, in the thirty years he survived Him, Jesus' aged cousin fed on that teaching with the ardor of a good man spurred by remorse. The guardian of the Law had also guarded the Sermon which contradicted the Law. "The ancients have told you, but I tell you. . . ."

Now there remained only John, the last pillar. And he will remain another thirty years: the youngest disciple will die a centenarian. Around him, too, history and legend weave aureoles of brilliance and darkness.

John landed in Asia after he escaped the boiling oil that would have made him a human torch in Rome. It was useless to go back to Jerusalem with James dead: Christianity went into exile; Rome abandoned, Jerusalem decayed, Antioch without leaders. The later added Ephesus became the temporary center of Christianity. John pitched his tents at Ephesus. After all, it was only fitting that it be the city where five centuries earlier Heraclitus had breathed presentiment of Christ.

The deacon Philip and his four prophesying daughters had arrived there from Caesarea before John. They, too, had aged.

For some time the two missionaries preached together, and they rose to great authority; by then they were the only survivors of Christianity's first muster. They became the two beacons of Asia. Philip's four daughters traveled through Phrygia, preaching particularly at Hierapolis, and in that last city they died and were buried. They had sowed so many prophesies in their journeying, and had gathered not a few miraculous flowers. Philip died, too, and only John was left, leader of all the churches.

Ephesus had formerly been Paul's, now it was half John's, half Paul's. And all the Asian churches Paul had founded were divided between his disciples and the later emissaries from Jerusalem. The moss and mold of heresy that had nestled in the cracks throve now.

Till that time John had lived in the meditation and sacrifice of a chaste secret life; his youth had not been expressed in action. Now in his declining years he came out into active life and found that the harsh battle was harsher still; his enemies multiplied. Peter, James, Barnabas, Luke, and the others had been good helmsmen elected to steer the vessel through treacherous but not stormy seas; John had to struggle against all the storms unleased by rash and senseless men. He must be the warrior.

Though he had escaped horrid death, he still bore in his soul all the terror engendered by the Neronian rabble. And the same terror was borne by those comrades in faith and misfortune who had left their family tatters and petty trades to attempt to rekindle a hearth fire where they could. But persecution followed them. The Neronian horde did not draw the curtain on the stage of Rome. Persecution of Christians raged and spread into every Mediterranean land, culminating in Domitian's reign between gusty winds and fair.

Fanaticism, in conjunction with profit, is monstrous in that it encourages the ferocious adoration of evil, of the malign. The

270

more Nero made himself hated and cursed, the more mad idolatry raved about him. The more beastly the beast became, the more people made him divine. In the Asiatic cauldron of obscene witchery, every sort of fanaticism seethed. When Nero died in Rome his myth was borne to Asia. A false Nero was seen at Citno in Parthia, and immediately found himself a court of mad and profligate adorers.

It was natural that after the fiendishness of men like Tiberius, Caligula, and Nero and their women and boys, mankind should believe the reign of Satan had arrived in the world. It was also logical and inevitable that with such a pack of unleashed hounds, the respect and reverence for Roman authority which Paul and Peter diplomatically urged on the faithful no longer existed in James. His emotion and counsel were directly descended from the anti-diplomacy of the ancient prohets, and thus the Apocalypse came into being.

The last apostle had withdrawn to the island of Patmos, seeking a spot in nature where he could nurse his scathing thoughts, possibly banished by imperial authority. He was still the head of the Ephesian church, completely Judaized now and augmented by the arrival of the remnants of the Roman colony that had escaped the slaughter. He was also the head of the six other important churches in Asia which retained little recollection of Paul: Smyrna, Pergamos, Thyatira, Sardis, Philadelphia, and Laodicea.

At Patmos, he wrote the Apocalypse, arcane prophecy of the imminence of the last days, illuminated and blinding revelation of Jesus Christ's second coming on earth. He sent it to the seven churches, and ordered it read and explained in each one. Enormous vision of a spirit consumed and an exalted fifty years of passion and meditation. He was a mere youth when Jesus died, but as happens with the very young, the Master's sentiments were deeply impressed on his soul; they burned him like a living fire. The proud certainty of being Jesus' favorite disciple grew inside him. He had fed his solitary life on that certainty and on the Mother's love perpetuating the Son's love. He had accepted the divine legacy Jesus entrusted to him as He approached death, and he guarded and defended it until the day when it, too, abandoned the earth.

That task filled his life for twenty years. He could not attend to another mission: there was no mission as important as this. To his comrades was left the task of bearing Jesus' word to faraway lands, among Jews and Gentiles: he had Jesus always present in Mary. He spoke of Him with her.

He had come out into action after Mary's death. His heart was swelled by all the restrained passion pressing on it. As no one else he had the truth stored up in him. His repressed thoughts burst out in glaring, stormy visions. Hope, secretly cultivated, exploded in whirlwinds of anathema. The youngest disciple had also been the boldest of Jesus' followers. When the "son of thunder," who had wanted to burn the unbelieving villages, began to add his voice to the others', Paul's particularly, it was indeed a voice of thunder that issued from his throat.

He wrote the Apocalypse when he was between seventy-five and eighty years old. He lived another twenty. He, too, wrote some letters and then, before his death, the fourth Gospel. Those of Matthew, Mark, and Luke had been circulating in all the churches for some years; they were the object of lessons and explanations to the neophytes in a liturgy which, through practice, was already developing its eventual form. Paul's letters also entered into the rite, bringing the theology of a more cultivated spirit trained in the investigation of the mystery. John wrote his Gospel to complete the simple and candid tale of the other three by lifting it into the realm of theory. It was also necessary to explain many of Paul's obscure sentences, which lent themselves to ambiguous interpretation.

He survived yet a few years to die the serene death of pure old age, without illness, in this perhaps the most fortunate of the disciples. His precept was "Who doesn't love his brother has not known God." Now his last words were an exhortation to love. "Love one another like brothers," he was wont to say to the young men who watched over his last moments until he had no breath left to continue. When they asked him to say something else, a spiritual legacy, he repeated only, "Love one another like brothers . . ." He could say no more.

And certainly man need say no more to mankind.

33

"If It Die"

And now history can resume its course alone.

Until now the Hebrew people, living between fear and terror, had feigned respect for constituted authority; now it was transformed into open rebellion. The Beast could not be obeyed. In Rome and in Asia Christians were dying for Christ; in Jerusalem the Jews will die for the temple.

This eternally-oppressed people now rebelled after a century of forbearance and rose against the yoke of Rome, and it was an insurrection not to be put down before the total extinction of their home.

Strange revolutions deranged nature, too, in those years—nature and men's brains. There were comets in the sky, tempests, apparitions of flying monsters, volcanic eruptions, and plagues. The people said that blood rained from clouds, rent like the bellies of enormous victims, that sudden fires broke out in the sanctuary's depths, that the great bronze doors of the temple opened by themselves and no human force could close them in preparation for the collective state of mind that would affront the supreme sacrifice. A Jesus of Anaias had already run through Jerusalem's streets crying, "Voice of the East! Voice of the West! Voice of the four winds! Voice against Jerusalem and the Temple! Voice against married men and women! Voice against the people! Woe, woe to Jerusalem!"

Reserves of hate and vengeance had accumulated underground in Palestine, and they lit the fire of popular insurrection. It started in Galilee and spread through Judea and Samaria. In the beginning it overcame the Roman resistance and gained power. Jerusalem and Caesarea were lost to the Empire. Then the Roman army recaptured control and crushed the revolution.

The Jewish spirit of independence, great virtue of that small people, reached excesses of fanaticism which could only find a term of comparison in the accesses of putrid fever that were making a madhouse of the Empire. These were exceeded only by the excesses of Roman cruelty in suppressing the rebellion. A people who had avoided every conflict with Rome for thirty years, and had hated Paul to the death because it feared that the herald of the Messiah would attract the imperial thunders, now burst free of its fear, or perhaps found the delirium of the holocaust in increased, inescapable, and interminable fear.

During Jesus' infancy, Judah of Gamala had attempted the first uprising over the question of taxes, and the Roman procurator's armored fist had destroyed him and his band. Now his descendants and heirs sought new leaders against the Romans, and they were led to their own complete extermination. A John of Giscala got possession of the temple, a Simon of Gioras made himself the commandant of Jerusalem. They were dragged as slaves behind the triumphal car of Vespasian and his son Titus. A nephew of Gamaliel, Eleazar, resisted for another two years on the rock of Masala in the Dead Sea; nor did he ever surrender. When he could no longer hold out, he and his nine hundred followers set fire to all their possessions and killed themselves.

The historian's statistics are bare and spectral like a limitless field of crosses. There was slaughter in Damascus, slaughter in Phrygia, slaughter in Egypt. A band of 6,700 zealots who sought to escape beyond the lake of Tiberias was drowned to the last man in the lake's waters. Another 1,200 were butchered in the city stadium, 6,000 sent to forced labor in the Isthmus of Corinth, 30,000 sold. In Galilee, 80,000 men were killed and 36,000 sold into slavery. Another million, one-hundred-thousand would die in Jerusalem; 97,000 were brought to Rome as prisoners, destined to slaughter each other in gladiators' games. Not a stone was left standing in the beautiful and holy city, which had received six of the seven parts of beauty which the Creator gave to His creation. Of the temple's massive construction only the foundation wall's few stones were left.

Nineteen centuries have to go by before the dispersed Jewish people will be struck by a like misfortune, and the world will see a similar destruction; before history registers analogous figures of Jews sent to destruction by the satanic madness of a miserable creature armed with steel and hatred.

After the death of the wise and just James, the Christians of Jerusalem realized that coexistence with the Jews was not easy. The bulwark fallen, no truce could be made between the zealots who tried to drown the rule of Rome in blood and the Christian faithful who shrugged off that rule with their indifference to worldly powers. These last felt the bloody city's pavements burning beneath their feet. Already the prophets had pointed out the road to salvation outside their country; now their leaders advised them to leave Jerusalem and take shelter in the desert mountains. They fled, followed by zealots, but they were able to ford the River Jordan and gather in the city of Pella.

Pella was a quiet city, far from all fighting and religious rivalry. A great many Christians took refuge there, and together with safe asylum, they found the undisturbed gentle warmth which gives rise to ideas and emotions.

Now Pella became the third source of Christianity, together with Rome, where the treetops but not the roots had been cut, and with Ephesus, center and mobilization point for all Asia. Those refugees brought with them the most limpid and genuine wellsprings in their prayers and songs which would gush directly into the pages of the Gospel—the Gospel of Matthew.

In Pella no echo of the old fights about the necessity or uselessness of the Law was heard. With Jerusalem and its temple fallen, the old trunk of conservative and legalistic Christianity rotted. Paul's revolutionary, theological offshoot sprouted from it, and the flowering stalk of the Gospel came to graft itself onto that shoot.

The disagreement which lasted for a while, especially in the Asian churches where it was irritated by the growing heresies, was not an ill in terms of history. We can think that if there had always been unanimous and united agreement, many small churches would have been lulled into inactivity, or would have lost vitality and been absorbed into the greater churches. The disagreement strengthened them, as the disease of growing strengthens the bones of the organism in formation. In every school or assembly the divergent opinions keep the opposing sides alive until one grows at the other's expense, unless they both grow in the same way; but it rarely happens that the one and the other perish in the impact or friction. It matters little that for a while this one rules that one, because even the side apparently ruled is leavened by the ruler and feeds on it. The

278

conservatism of Jerusalem had been necessary for the development of the Pauline revolution.

Jerusalem's end accelerated the leavening process in the Church's breast so much that this moment can be considered the new beginning of Christianity. Besides being a vain exercise of the mind, it is difficult to imagine what would have happened to the Church of Christ if the Roman Empire had not destroyed Jerusalem. History does not stop on its journey to gather hypotheses let fall by restless men's imaginations; it follows the immutable course of events. The destruction of Jerusalem removed the major obstacle—which was almost a legal obstacle—to the construction of Christianity. Poetry sees a mother die after giving birth to her immortal child.

But what does history matter after all, history which at this point embarks on a road full of mists, a road that only the ray of poesy can illuminate? History loads its train only with men who have a name and events which have a date, but unfairly ignores the anonymous men who drive that train and the events that have fallen to the roadside. Legend ignores them too. Paul, Peter, John, Luke, Matthew, Mark, Barnabas, and their disciples were architects of genius, remembered and glorified by history and legend. We now see again the enormous crowd of the anonymous, which we had already seen at the beginning of our tale—artisans, workmen, laborers—each of whom laboriously brought a stone, a trowel of cement, a bag of sand, or a board to the great works risen first around an uncovered tomb at the foot of Mount Calvary and then enlarged to the farthest boundaries of the known world. Paul too says that their names are written in the book of life, though excluded from the book of history.

No harm in looking at the written chronicles and oral traditions through the incorruptible lens called poetry, to try to discover hidden composition and movements of events and men, for they cannot be perceived by the historian's naked eye.

Perhaps someone still lived who as a child had seen Jesus and had heard some of those great words swell like a song in the air there on the hills of the Beatitudes, or on the poppy-strewn shores of Gennesaret Lake, or heard them thunder out terribly under the temple porticos where Levites and scribes were trafficking. There were those who had known Peter, James, and John and the other nine, and had begged them to recount something of what they knew, the secret of allusive parables revealed only to them ("who has ears to hear, let him hear"), and the other smooth and severe words Jesus had said to a woman in Samaria at Jacob's Well, to a young adulteress struck by stones on the road of the Golden Gate, or those Jesus had used in a stormy night on the lake, or at a feast in the house of the wedding at Cana, or during a day of mourning on the road to Naim. . . .

They had known Mary, Martha, Salome, or Suzanna and, from those pious women who knew everything, they had learned how the Divine Master had been crucified, died, and been resurrected. The youngest had not known those old men and the pious women, but they had gathered the voices that every rustle of trees in the wind seemed to spread through the air. Fathers told their sons on their way to work in the field, or while they rested in the hayfield under the shade of a great sycamore. The potter and the weaver told the stranger who came to buy in their shops. The fishermen of Tiberias repeated the tales as they mended their nets in the sun, as did the publicans at the counters of the customshouse where Matthew once sat. Women confided them to each other under the portico as they ground the wheat for their bread. Through them the new religion spread with the silent effusion of oil, to use the image of Plato.

Wandering folk had borne and would continue to bear those words to every country in the world, where they stopped to ask a night's hospitality, or to stay and found a family, in the same way that the first fruits of a new garden are brought to market. They had brought them before Paul, before Peter, before John (they met these last on their journey and sheltered them); and they bring them afterward too, to him who comes. How many things those wayfarers know which the others ask to hear. They are not sermons, but confidences. With the rapidity of confidences, they penetrate the capillary vessels of domestic intimacy. They fill every house and hut with new voices which speak of love. It is as if an infinite blooming of voices spreads over the earth, as if the heavens had poured down all their stars, and every star had revealed a voice.

Thus the mustard seed becomes the biggest plant in the field. Every confidence locked in the secret heart is already a conviction.

The church has not been able to collect all those scattered voices under its canons, as the reaper leaves wheat which has fallen from his scythe to the gleaners when he binds and piles his sheaves. But from that fallen and abandoned grain good bread is made—the bread of the poor. And those candid and ingenuous voices breathe eternal spirit into the monument built by the Gospels and the Letters.

This was the dawn wind which kept the wavering taper of the disciples lit and spread its flame throughout the world; and the light of martyrdom creates a visionary enchantment.

No human power of word and action has a comparable effect on spirits softened by pain, and never had the world been so hurt and sorrowful. The sight of young men and women offering the flower of their youth for an idea which goes beyond death exalts the imagination and inspires the emotions to mystic emulation. The torment of that tender flesh still warm with life, of those limbs created for the joy of love, and made for the energy of work, creates a yearning for the ecstasy of suffering which surpasses and annihilates all other existences. To die, to torment, becomes the supreme joy. At their trials, innocents are seen to declare themselves guilty and to prefer death to freedom. The persecutions made more proselytes than prizes and promises had made. Before the century was over the three thousand of the first Pentecost were hundreds of thousands. The soldiers' legions had conquered an empire for Rome; the martyrs' legions will conquer the world for Christ.

A new generation of believers germinated from every martyr's tomb. Where the blood of their bodies was poured out, fountains of fresh water flowed: "Unless the grain of wheat fall into the ground and die, itself remaineth alone; but if it die, it bringeth forth much fruit."

The Author
and His Book

THE AUTHOR AND HIS BOOK

Michele Saponaro was born in San Cesario, Italy, in 1885. He studied at the University of Naples; however, his studies were interrupted by World War I, during which time he served in the army. He initiated his literary career with the publication of short stories. His first novel, *The Vigil* (1914), gained great critical acclaim, and the coming of age of a new literary master was heralded. This work was followed by *Peccato* (1919), *Fiorella* (1920), *Nostra Madre* (1921), *Adolescenze* (1924), *La Bella Risvegliata* (1927), *Io E Mia Moglie* (1929), *La Città Felice* (1934), and *Il Cerchio Magico* (1938).

Since 1937, Saponaro has dedicated himself to the writing of biographical works; having written the lives of Foscolo (1938), Carducci (1940), Leopardi (1942), Mazzini (1944), and Michelangelo (1947); all of which, in the opinion of one of Italy's most illustrious critics, are outstanding examples of a rare combination of story-telling ability and a true talent for biography. The best-known and most important of his works to date are *Gesú* and *I Discepoli,* both of which are sheer poetic prose, related with true fervor for the spirit and fact of the times. Both books are widely known through the various translations which have appeared; this book is a translation of *I Discepoli.*

THE FISHERS OF MEN (Hawthorn Books, 1962) is set in

Granjon type, which was designed for the Linotype under the direction of George W. Jones. This typeface was named for the French type designer, Robert Granjon. The type was set and the book printed by letterpress by the Hamilton Printing Company, Rensselaer, New York. It was bound by the Montauk Book Manufacturing Company, Inc., New York City.

A HAWTHORN BOOK